The Bounce Back Journey of Women's Health

AN INSPIRING COLLECTION OF PERSONAL STORIES

Compiled by
Discover Your Bounce Publishing

DEDICATION

When writing a book about women, for women, we wondered who we could approach as an icon and inspirational advocate for women, globally and we approached friend of Team Bounce Dr Harbeen Arora. Dr Harbeen is the Global Chairperson for ALL Ladies League and Women Economic Forum (WEF) where both Sharon and Nicky have spoken.

On Women:

"Our Wisdom as Women comes from our immeasurable capacity for Change, Adjustment and Adaptation, empowering our spirit of survival and grace of evolution. We are Mother Nature's daughters, blessed by Her infinite powers of Healing and Wholesomeness. As Infinite Beings with Intelligent Bodies, Trust your Capacity to Heal and Transition into another level of Wholesomeness at all times."

On Health (I'm an Ayurveda evangelist!!):

"Inner Harmony is key to our chemistry of Health and Wellness. The Subtle realities of our Spirit give rise to counterpart physical Manifestations. Guard Your Mind with the Medication of Meditation. Invigorate your Heart with Faith and Forgiveness. Support Your Strength and Renewal with Mother Nature's Healing Herbs. Live with the Self-Assurance of being Eternal and Infinite. Love your Unique Journey. Practice Patience. Be Kind to Yourself."

All the best!
Warmest, Harbeen

Dr. Harbeen Arora
Founder, BIOAYURVEDA www.bioayurveda.in
Global Chairperson, ALL Ladies League (ALL) www.aall.in &
Women Economic Forum (WEF) www.wef.org.in
Founder President, WICCI, Women's Indian Chamber of Commerce and Industry www.wicci.in
Founder, SHEconomy www.sheconomy.in

CONTENTS

FOREWORD
By Nicky Marshall

I would like to tell you about a wonderful lady called Vanessa. When I opened my coffee shop and holistic centre in 2010, I was first to encounter Vanessa. She quietly sat on my sofa and ordered a cappuccino, while deliberating over her choice of cake.

When it came to closing time, Vanessa asked me to help her up and that was the first of many requests. You see, Vanessa had a condition called Scleroderma; an awful condition with a host of mobility and muscular challenges and completely debilitating…for most. In the beginning, the Scleroderma had even impacted her smile.

Vanessa was not like most sufferers, she was a proud Yorkshire lass with a great sense of humour, a huge heart, a passion for cats, a yearning to own a whippet one day and a spirit that meant she was not going to lie down and accept any limitation…not without a big fight anyway. Her quiet behaviour on that first day gave way to hours of chatting, laughter and a few tears.

Over the months and years, we spent hours talking about life (and eating cake). We talked about the Law of Attraction, manifesting, crystals…oh and sport and boys! Vanessa had Reiki and Reflexology treatments from me and worked with several other therapists who ran their businesses from our premises, including Louise Morgan, who was to be a constant support and friend to Vanessa.

Over time, she regained her smile, got back a lot of mobility and finally took home her lovely whippet puppy called Zara. Along with a cat called Jamie, her family was complete.

From time to time she took a tumble and would ask me to take a photo to document the occasion. She would get health scares and setbacks too, but never accepted that anything would slow her down.

Two weeks ago, I received a message that Vanessa had suffered a cardiac arrest, to which I responded by asking how she was. It appeared that Vanessa had in fact died instantly, in the hairdressers she loved.

I hadn't been in touch recently. I had been out for her 60th birthday a couple of years ago and we had met up last summer. We always kept in touch through Facebook and she would often tag me in posts of dishy men that she found! But for a couple of years I had the pleasure of seeing a lot of Vanessa and she changed my life.

When I suffered the stroke in 2010, I had Vanessa to inspire me. Vanessa embodied the spirit of bouncing back, never giving in, always trying to smile and always there to offer advice, knowledge or a helping hand. Her 'Sod 'em!' attitude towards anyone who put her down or tried to tell her how her life would be was a true inspiration. So many friends and customers remembered Vanessa for her smile and wit.

So it seems fitting, while writing about women's health and the ability to bounce back, that we dedicate this book to Vanessa. In the coming pages you will read more amazing stories. I believe that every one of us has within us the ability to bounce – if we have the right tools and the support around us. I invite you to enjoy this book, over a cuppa at the weekend wrapped in a blanket or as a positivity reset on a busy day.

Vanessa, fly high my friend…until we meet again.

AMI MORRISON

Ami is in her late-20s, living in Belfast with her husband and baby. She is currently discovering life as a new mother and navigating the perils of sleep deprivation. In her spare time (if she gets any!) she is a proof-reader and editor for Discover Your Bounce Publishing.

Ami is passionate about creating the life you want and overcoming obstacles, even when they seem impossible.

You can reach Ami through the Discover Your Bounce team: info@discoveryourbounce.com

Let's Be Honest

I'm currently falling apart. I know that doesn't really sound very inspiring, but bear with me.

If you've read any of the other Missing Piece books you might know some of my history; I was diagnosed with two autoimmune conditions in my early 20s and had an upsetting, but ultimately successful, infertility journey that gave me my first child last year.

If you read those chapters, you might even have assumed that my next one would continue the story. I had certainly planned to. But, you see, I'm currently falling apart. I hadn't planned to write about it, but I sat down to write and here we are. Talking about it.

We need to do that more, I think.

Mental health has become the latest thing, everyone is talking about it, so you might be confused by that statement. Let me clarify: *we need to talk about our own mental health more.*

When was the last time you had an honest conversation with someone about your mental health? If it was recently then brilliant! How honest were you? Was it at a time you were struggling? How honest are you when you're falling apart?

I think that's where we need to put more of our focus. It's become okay to say we're struggling, but we also need to know how to elaborate. How to say, "I see no way out of this." Or, "This is so all-encompassing that I don't have the energy to [insert personal care activities here]."

There's almost a 'media friendly' version of mental illness. Being honest about not feeling your best self right now, but not so honest that it can't be fixed with an inspirational image and a 'care' emoji on Facebook. We wouldn't want to scare people away, would we?

So, let's go there, stranger reading this book. Let's get honest about mental health and not worry about how we'll look, or what people will think. I'll go first.

I see no way out of this. It's become so all-encompassing that I don't sleep well at night (even worse than my tiny human allows) and I only brush my hair when I'm about to wash it. Let's face it, that tiny human is only going to have it in knots 5 minutes later anyway... Yesterday I showered for the first time in I actually can't remember how long. Surviving and keeping my mental health from affecting my child was taking all of my energy. I've been distant with my husband and trying not to start arguments I didn't mean,

4

but starting them anyway in my attempts to avoid them. I've been spending too much time on my phone after a night feed when I should be sleeping because I can't shut my brain off.

That's just the start; the stuff I can think of off the top of my head. At nearly 10 months post-partum, the obvious assumption is that I'm struggling with Post Natal Depression. I'm not though. That's a story that needs to be told too, but it's not mine. I am just in the middle of a ****-storm of many things colliding at once.

This chapter is a bit depressing so far, isn't it? But that's kind of the point. Here's the turnaround:

This morning I talked to my husband. We had another silence-filled argument because I'd tried to avoid one, again, and said completely the wrong thing, again. This time though, I was honest afterwards. I told him all of my struggles and didn't hold back. My health worries, how overwhelmed I was with our house-hunting attempts, the fact that I can't seek medical attention for my conditions because of a global pandemic... I put all of my cards on the table. There were tears, not all of them mine.

This afternoon we took not one, but two steps forward towards a solution. Steps I just couldn't see because I was thinking myself in circles. I was too lethargic to think most of the time and when I could think I was held captive by decision paralysis. Talking to someone else was exactly what I needed to see my first step back to mental wellbeing.

I've been here before so I'm not naive enough to think everything is better now, but having my husband on board is such a relief. He's no longer in the dark when I'm distant or needing yet another morning off. He's also being more honest with me. Not about his own mental health, but with the other thing we don't talk about often enough: *how great we think other people are.*

I don't see my own worth right now. To be honest, I feel a bit of a burden to those who have to listen to me complain all the time. But he sees my worth and has been reminding me all day, along with providing chocolate and hugs. It's nice to hear. I hope to believe him soon.

I've overcome mental health struggles plenty of times before and it has always started with opening up, being honest and getting a support system in place. Whether that's a friend, a family member or a medical professional where needed.

So now it's your turn, stranger reading this. Time to be honest. You don't have to be struggling – don't hide how great you're doing either! Tell your mum. Tell your partner. Tell your best friend, or all of your friends! Tell your doctor. Good, bad, brilliant, terrifying. Share it all and see what being honest can do for you.

AMY BLYTHE

I have a huge passion for all things self-care. I aim to inspire and educate about the importance of practicing daily self-care through my business. As well as being a self-care advocate, I teach yoga and am a sports massage therapist. I'm going to become a Wellness Coach one day soon! I love yoga and running, gardening, being by the sea, reading, drinking coffee, journaling and spending time with my family! I'm a proud mum of two daughters and I've lived in Devon for the last 18 years.

www.amyblythe.co.uk

https://instagram.com/amyblytheyoga/

https://facebook.com/amyblythemassageyoga

https://twitter.com/amyaimfit

Shamelessly Me

When I'm having me-time on my favourite beach in the sun, post-run with a coffee, life is pretty blinkin' good! I'm really lucky. I have two beautiful daughters and a partner who loves and supports me in everything I do. My family live close by and show me endless love and support. My friends are great, crazy, funny, beautiful all in their own individual ways, plus they let me be their friend! I live in a beautiful part of the world, I love my job, I am my own boss and I'm healthy and happy. That's why it never made any sense as to why I suffered with anxiety.

It wasn't there all the time, but when it came it usually came from nowhere. There is the odd time when it rears its head and I can go, "Ok. Cool. Yup, I don't much like this situation so it's ok to feel anxious," but usually it's out of the blue.

It's my hope that one day my anxiety will completely disappear, never to return, but I know that's probably not going to happen. After all, we need anxiety in our lives. Anxiety is an essential part of our survival. We'd be a reckless crew without it. My understanding, and it's by no means scientific, is this:

Anxiety is normal. It's a protection response. We need it to survive.

However, mine sometimes doesn't know when to stop; it has lost its' trip switch! So, I need to act as the trip switch.

Brené Brown is a brilliant storyteller and research professor studying shame, vulnerability, courage and empathy. She tells us that, "Owning our story and loving ourselves through that process is the bravest thing that we will ever do." I completely understand and appreciate this.

I never spoke about the issues I had with anxiety. The only people who really knew were my partner, my parents and sister and one or two friends who I knew would 'get it'. For years I saw my anxiety as a weakness. I didn't want to be like that. I wanted be fit and strong and able to deal with whatever life threw at me. So, I tried to pretend it wasn't there. I certainly wouldn't admit to it. But if **you** were to tell me that **you** suffer with anxiety and **you** are talking about it – that you were facing it and not letting it rule you or beat you – I'd think you were amazing and strong! It's funny how we treat ourselves so differently isn't it?

The first memory I have of my anxiety was about 16 years ago. An awareness that if I didn't make myself breathe, I wasn't going to breathe. Silly, right? Breathing is an unconscious process that the body just does. But once I'd tuned into this perceived inability to breathe, that was it. That became the thing my mind focused on and so I would over-breathe and in effect I'd be hyperventilating. My worst time for this would be when I was driving. I love driving, I'm a fairly good driver (I think), but that was the time it would start. It made no sense to me.

The other symptom that used to rear its head was a strong, hard, fast heartbeat. That sensation has to be one of the worst. It is still the one I contend with today. It will come from nowhere, often in the middle of the night, just to remind me it's still there!

There were no real triggers for my anxiety, the trigger would simply be the symptoms; my heart popping out of my chest and the inability to breathe were enough to raise my anxiety levels! No surprise there then.

Over the following years my anxiety came and went with varying degrees of intensity and symptoms. At its worst I even stopped going to the gym, convinced that I would have a heart attack on the treadmill. Running is a go-to self-care practice for me, so at this point my anxiety was affecting my coping strategies as well. The anxiety that I struggled with was health related anxiety, so I was basically a hypochondriac! I really struggled with this label. But no one, apart from myself, labelled me that to my face and for that I'm grateful.

I'd go to the doctors all the time with crazy symptoms, which I turned into life threatening conditions. I was in a vicious circle; weird symptom - go to the doctor - seek reassurance - feel better… for a week - new weird symptom (or same symptom, what if they missed something?) - go to the doctor - seek reassurance - feel better for a week… and so it went on. I hated this too. I knew I was wasting the doctor's time, but I knew I'd feel better for a bit. I was really lucky to have a sympathetic and lovely GP, who took me seriously, let me cry and then would laugh with me.

From the outside I would generally function well; being a Mum, running my business, running the house (although not so good at the cleaning, but I can't really blame that on anxiety!) On the inside however, a lot of the time it was a different story. I'd obsess. I'd worry. I'd spend a lot of time being frightened. I'd fear the worst. I'd catastrophise. It was tiring! I also struggled with the selfishness I perceived that I had; it's all about me after all!

Every life experience is a lesson. Another quote I love, this time from Marie Forleo, is, "I win or I learn but I never lose." It means that you get to choose how you can learn and rise from that stumble or that knockback. She makes clear that the lesson isn't always obvious immediately and that's ok, but with the gift of time, you **can** find that lesson.

I have found my lesson. Self-care was my lesson. I became vulnerable and courageous and began to tell the world about my anxiety. I realised the importance of self-care. My self-care journey began with the realisation that by taking better care of myself I had some minute control over this anxiety. Any small control over my anxiety was a win. I practiced self-reflection, acceptance and self-awareness, to really get to know myself and to learn what I need to make my heart sing and for me to smile inside. I stopped feeling shame about my anxiety.

Maintaining 'normal' levels of anxiety is a life's work for me. I know I'm susceptible to bouts of anxiety and that's ok. Self-care has become my passion. I want to tell everyone to slow down and move yourself higher up your to-do list. You matter. You are important. And actually, if you take care of yourself first then you are better equipped to take care of those around you, the people you love.

The best analogy for this is the oxygen mask. Each time you fly, you listen to the flight attendants telling you that in case of an emergency, place your mask on before that of your child. As a Mum, this used to make me go, "Whaaaat?!" But actually, if you don't put your mask on and help yourself first, you will be in no position to help your child! It's no different in daily life. Simple really.

My journey with anxiety has done so much for me. I found a passion for writing as a way to help myself and others. I discovered a passion for self-care and a desire to share its importance. I want to inspire people to practice daily self-care. To remind them it's not selfish or a luxury, but a necessity, an essential component of wellbeing and good mental health.

I do this through my yoga teaching, my sports massage (a lot of talking happens here!), a little bit of blogging and sharing my thoughts on social media. I was recently asked to present a webinar to a local law firm on self-care. A paid gig to talk about something I love to talk about. How lucky am I? I am hosting an Expo to promote, educate and inspire people about self-care and wellness; a day full of wonderful like-minded people who I have connected with. I haven't done this before but my passion and commitment seem to shine through and people have jumped on board. Would I have done any of this without my experience with anxiety? I don't know, I really don't.

Life throws us curveballs all the time. It's part of this awesome adventure we are on. As Jon Kabat-Zinn said, "You can't stop the waves but you can learn how to surf." Anxiety will come and go for me, but I need to remember it won't control me. It won't last forever. Breathe and I will be ok.

Be kind to yourself.

Live your best life.

Be whoever you want to be.

Breathe.

You will be ok.

ANCA PETCU BHATTI

Anca is a rebel: she ran away from home at the age of 14 to be an independent woman. She prefers to work behind the scenes for what she believes is fair and just. Although she is willing to take centre stage for a cause that is important enough to her, like founding the first eco cleaning business and choosing to be the first Living Wage employer in this sector in Bristol, UK. She is now an ambassador for this cause, working with businesses to take the step to offering better employment.

Anca's innocent, unwavering optimism speaks to our needs for simpler times, wholesomeness and honest values. She is a loyal cheerleader for female entrepreneurs, especially eco-mumpreneurs.

www.ancapb.com

https://facebook.com/ancasecofriendlyservices

https://linkedin.com/in/anca-petcu-1534b344/

https://instagram.com/ancapetcubhatti/

What Would You Do With Five More Years?

Anca is an overly determined eco-mumpreneur, originally from Bucharest in Romania. In November 2009 she decided to move across Europe, from the very far East to the very far West of the continent to Bristol, UK.

Anca had just £40 in her pocket, 2 twenty pound notes to be exact. With her were her three children: Sonia, Joshua and Alin who at that time were 6, 2 and 6 months old.

Shortly after this, in January 2010, she had the realisation that she also must change her career path. While her English was good, she would need to learn English for osteopath terms.

With extensive business experience from Romania, she decided to put her best skills to work and Eco Cleaning Bristol was founded. Due to her ability to strive for excellence the business has grown rapidly and started to provide work for others.

A few years later after a routine cervical screening test she was referred to the hospital for further investigation.

Hey my darling reader, my name is Anca and until this point in my story it felt easier to write like I would write about somebody else as it doesn't feel like showing off!

I see myself as probably the simplest person in the world and on top of that I love simplicity. The simpler things can be the better.

However, I was used to being shown off. I was brought up in the capital of an ex-Communist country and my father has been a director of an important factory for over 30 years. Often, when visiting my loving grandparents in the countryside, I had to always be a show off.

In the capital I was always 'the Directors daughter,' attending one of the best schools in the country at that time and having a driver take me to school. In the countryside during the school holidays I was the 'city girl,' so Anca actually rarely existed.

I now live happily in a council estate in Southmead, with my three children and my incredibly handsome Punjabi husband, Randip.

I feel I can honestly say that the last lines which I've just written were definitely another attempt of my mind and body to avoid the pain of what I am about to tell you.

I'm sat here in my tiny living room, at my beautifully upcycled oak table which was gifted to us by a generous customer, and now friend, Margaret. The sun is shining through the window as it's just about to set and I am warmly being accompanied by the golden hour.

I'm stuck. How do I go further in sharing with you how I have bounced back from seeing the end of my life?

There is pressure in my head, slight numbness in my face, my tummy is like a rock and words have suddenly seemed to vanish from my brain.

Taking a deep breath and one, no two more!

The doctors were polite, doing their best to not say the C word and, as a straight talker and a single mother at the time, I really, really needed to know facts.

I said, "Look, I don't have time for 'let's see X, Y or Z.' I am a single mother of three children currently on my way to homelessness as I am being evicted by my Landlord."

(Oh, didn't I mention that I was going through eviction as well?)

"I have to know what is going on as I have to plan."

The doctor said, "Anca in the best case scenario you have a maximum of another five years to live."

I said, "Okay, thank you, bye!"

The doctor begged me not to go and to just sit on a chair in the hospital hallway, as apparently the nurse needed to talk to me. She didn't really, but the whole team was terrified to let me go home as I was on my own.

The warmth of that nurse was incredible and I remember seeing the joy on her face when she was talking about her son. I think she said he was in his 20's, which seemed so powerful that I burst into a massive, deafening cry.

"I really, really need to live at least another 7 years so my daughter can be 18 years old. Then she can legally care for her younger brothers, so they do not end up in an orphanage!" is all I recall saying to the nurse.

I cannot remember how I went home from the hospital. Thinking about it now, my body and my mind seemed to get a strong, clear sense of all the feelings which flooded every single cell of my tiny human body.

I then went into rocket mode, turning myself into a stone with no feelings allowed; to just focus on getting the little people in my life to a point where they could care for themselves. My threshold for anything that wasted my time rose to 300% and my focus narrowed to an extreme where only this mattered.

Once home, Mirela (a young loving mother who would mind the children while I was working), greeted me and said the children were already in bed.

I felt released, as at least for that moment I didn't feel like I had to hide my emotions again.

Mirela left and I remember putting a post on Facebook looking to find out more information from someone who might have been in the same situation. In the next minute or so there was a knock on the door and my friends, Anita and Tracy had come to see me.

It was so good, they were very kind and warm and there to hold me up mentally and physically. I found myself repeating to them what I had said to the nurse. My whole being, including my brain, was consumed by my main and only desire.

After they made sure I was okay, they left and I went on Facebook to check if there were any comments on my post with information. Sadly, there were none with the information I was looking for, however the post was full of comments from family and friends who hadn't bothered about me or the children in the previous years. Now they suddenly remembered us?

It made me incredibly angry. Really, really angry; so I deleted the post.

Why on earth would people think it's okay to message you or suddenly care about you, especially in this tough moment when you can barely keep yourself together?

I was not looking for anyone's pity, I only wanted information so I could figure out how tomorrow and the days ahead might look.

Their comments and messages made me feel disabled, it translated to me that there was something wrong with me. At the time I barely had enough time to go and earn a living, let alone reply to people's messages and comments.

From that day I became a completely different person. My thinking changed to extremes and everything in my life started to get the filter of, "If I knew I would die tomorrow, what would I do?" Even if it was about something as simple as a cake, I would still ask myself the same question.

At the time I was not driving and I was still working from 8am until 6pm. There were days when I would finish at 10pm; all this while my main mode of transport was a push bike.

A couple of days after my visit to the hospital, I received a letter saying that my results had been sent to a different hospital to be seen by another specialist. They said they would contact me in about two weeks.

Every day became a gift.

I was cycling to work and thinking, 'Whatever happens today I'll be happy and when I get home I'll celebrate with the children.' And I surely did.

I am the kind of person that does not need a reason to celebrate. The weeks went quickly by and the letter from the specialist came. It had great news; from their point of view I only needed LELTZ operations (Large Loop excision of the transformation zone), not chemotherapy or radiotherapy. This is less invasive, as the damaged tissue is removed using a thin wire loop that is heated electrically.

However great this news was, my situation was so tough that having to take a day off work to be in hospital was not possible. I had to choose between my health and earning money to feed the children and pay the rent.

I did choose to go for my first operation and from that day the debt started to grow. Although the operations were only for a day at a time, I also had to have at least another day after to rest.

The pressure from work was starting to build up as I was missing days and, being self-employed, nobody would pay if I was sick.

The children's father was unreliable as always and my family were definitely not in a position to help in any way. I remember sitting at the dining room table and I now think that I must have been in an extreme state of depression at the time. I had no clue what was going on with me, my mind was up in the clouds and I can't recall any feelings.

Our eviction was getting closer and all I could think to do was to keep going.

After a few consecutive operations, our eviction and our new house, an army of friends, schoolteachers and church members arrived. All pulling together and doing everything possible for us to be in a better place; things were starting to look up.

We were now in a council house where the rent was half of that compared to what we were paying privately. My operations were only every three months, so I slowly managed to get myself out of debt over the following year.

Our new house was in a very poor state when it was given to us. At the time the council, by law, was only required to provide you with a safe kitchen and bathroom. The rest of the house, without exaggeration, was a ghetto.

We had managed to clean one room and we only had one double and one single mattress on the floor for the four of us, but we were really happy.

Whereas before I could only see eviction ahead of me, a maximum of five years to my life and going into debt, rapidly things started to go uphill.

My children were now safely in the house they could call HOME and my treatments were reducing. To be honest I was not quite sure why I was still being treated as 90% of my cervix had been removed previously, but hey, I had many more things to be grateful for.

In general I am a very positive person and most of the time I see the half full part of the glass. I am very good at counting my blessings. I am not sure that I can say that I was counting my blessings through my tough time as I can't remember.

I definitely remember my new style of prayer, I am a Christian and Jesus is my best friend. Bless Jesus, as only he knows how many times he's been told off, shouted at and God knows what else!

I remember pushing my bike up the hill after a day of work, as I didn't have the strength to cycle anymore and singing prayers.

Although there was no need for more operations, my cervical screening in itself was an operation. Every 6 months I had to be admitted to hospital for the day and have the 10% of my cervix left cut open etc.

Not sure why they left 10% of it in there as I already had three kids too many anyway, hehe!

From this chapter of my life I have learnt that it is impetuously necessary to trust myself, to switch on my faith to its highest volume and be grateful for everything I've learned.

BEATRICE MARTIN

Bea's been interested in health for most of her life, particularly when a health crisis in her 20s propelled her into discovering more about complementary health therapies.

With jobs ranging from being on the Corporate Management Team of two general hospitals in her late 20s to now practising as a sound therapist, the wellbeing of others has often been at the core of her work.

She's had several articles on health and wellbeing published internationally, both in magazines and online.

Based in the South West of England, she lives and works with her partner David as part of the duo Bards of Avalon. When they were both 50, they released their first album and have been working full-time as sound therapists since 2010. Like wandering minstrels, they also love to guide others around sacred sites with storytelling and live musical accompaniment. They are currently writing a book about their adventures.

www.bardsofavalon.com

Abnormal

Abnormal.

The word leapt out from the letter amidst a haze of typewritten characters.

Abnormal cells.

As my eyes focused more these words demanded my full attention, shaking me to my core. The results of my smear test had come back showing early stages of cervical cancer. Looking back, I wasn't in fear about this news or the possibility that this could be life-threatening. What I did feel was anger. How could this have happened when I was on my own and had not had a partner for eight years?

I needed to have a further investigation called a colposcopy to determine what was going on with my cervix. The colposcopy revealed the inflamed tissue of pre-cancerous cells. I felt like part of me was rotting away due to underuse. I was given the option of cryotherapy treatment which sounded like something out of a science fiction movie, but basically involved freezing off the abnormal cells.

A friend offered to drive me to the hospital and accompany me for the procedure. It was a kind offer which I eagerly accepted. However, I began to regret the decision as my friend continually complained that it was taking so long to be seen and she needed to get on with other things.

I was conscious throughout the process which felt extremely painful. The area was then painted over with silver nitrate to further cauterise the abnormal cells. It felt like I'd been hit by a truck. I staggered out of the hospital, protectively clutching my belly as though my insides depended on it.

I had frequent cervical smear tests for the next two years, all coming back with 'abnormal' results. Eventually a doctor said matter-of-factly, "You'd be better off having a hysterectomy." Stunned into silence by this bombshell news, I left the consulting room in profound shock. I couldn't believe it. This wasn't a simple procedure like removing a wart, this affected my foundations as a woman. Suddenly the choice to have children was being taken away and I would be plunged into a premature menopause.

With a Spanish father and Italian mother, I was brought up as a Catholic in a household where children were a very important part of Mediterranean culture. A woman isn't truly a woman until she has children of her own and provides the gift of grandchildren for her parents. Being the eldest of five children, I found myself responsible for my siblings from a very early age. There's a photo of me when I was 12 with my brothers and sister; I look like their mother. Even my youngest brother used to call me 'Ma-ma'. I love children, am a very enthusiastic aunty, and have spent most of my life in caring roles. I just had a deep inner knowing that I wasn't meant to have children of my own.

Of course, this went totally against the culture and my upbringing. It wasn't that I was particularly career minded, I'd just had enough of parenting my siblings and my parents. I felt cheated of my childhood and adolescence and wanted more say in my adulthood.

Born in the late 50s, I grew up in the 60s when the perfect woman was portrayed as a dutiful wife who looked immaculately glamorous. She stayed at home, cared for children, had a spotlessly clean home with dinner ready for her husband when he returned from work and said nothing apart from tending to her husband's needs. The pressure to conform to this ideal of perfection was very real for my mother and other women of her generation.

My ex-husband and I agreed before we married that we didn't want children. My ex-mother-in-law was forever knitting baby clothes in vain and my mother was always making comments about depriving her of grandchildren. When I met others and was asked if I had any children and replied no, I was often met with "Oh, what a shame, you could always adopt or foster. Who will look after you when you get old?"

With the prospect of a hysterectomy, the choice to have children was being removed from me. Even though I knew deep down I wasn't meant to have children, this felt wrong on so many levels. I knew with every cell of my being that I had to find a way to heal that wouldn't involve such radical, invasive surgery.

As anyone who knew me at that time could attest, there was nothing about my life that was 'normal'. I'd stepped away from the 'normal' world of a permanent full-time job, company car and mortgaged home in 1997.

The time between that first test results letter in 1998 to the hysterectomy chat with the doctor in 2000 was one of the most unconventional and extraordinary times in my life. I remember one day realising that I had no keys to a home, car or anything else. It was both disconcerting yet liberating at the same time.

During this time I worked at a retreat centre in Glastonbury, went to the USA to learn more about sound therapy, volunteered in eco-communities in Wales, Colorado and Los Angeles and had a number of contractor jobs including working on a construction site in Amsterdam.

I then found myself back at my father's home in London, sleeping on the sofa. I was trying to get the money to get a place of my own. In those days the best paid contractor jobs were in Canary Wharf. It was an exciting time to be there and witness the dramatic transformation of neglected docklands into a glitzy, thriving business hub. However, my initial excitement began to wane as I worked longer hours. My daily routine would consist of getting up around 5.00 am each day, commute to Canary Wharf, start work at 7.30 am and finish around 6.00 pm. I wouldn't get back till 7.30 pm. It seemed a never-ending treadmill.

Then I received a phone call out of the blue that would change my life.

It was my friend Pam. A few years' previously we'd had a joint birthday party. Amongst the guests, Pam had invited her friend Eunice. I'd not met Eunice before but was immediately drawn to her radiance and joyful, calm presence. However, we hardly spoke that evening as I was busy hosting.

Pam said she had a message from Eunice: "I don't know what's going on for Bea right now, but just let her know if she ever needs to have some time out, rest and recharge, she's very welcome to my home in France for as long as she wants." On hearing this news, I burst into tears. Here was a virtual stranger opening her home to me at a time when I most needed it.

I knew I needed to stop. My work contract was ending in July, so I headed off to France as soon as that finished.

Eunice lived in a former forge; a beautiful stone house nestled amidst the foothills of the Pyrenees in southern France, close to the Spanish border. It's an enchanting area with Carcassonne's fairy tale turrets, legends of the Holy Grail in Rennes le Chateau and a spectacular landscape to make your heart sing. There's something about mountainous regions where one can literally take a more elevated perspective on one's life. It couldn't have been in sharper contrast to the futuristic glass, steel and concrete of the Manhattan-on-Thames I'd become accustomed to.

The gentle rhythm and pace of life there meant I could finally stop. I didn't realise how exhausted I was. I seemed to sleep for days; I certainly needed it. Since I'd stepped away from the 'normal' world of corporate life, I hadn't really settled anywhere. Whilst I'd had an exciting time with some amazing experiences and met inspirational people, the constant travelling had taken a toll on my body. I had to face the reality that I was 41 and didn't have the boundless energy I had when I was younger.

Each day, Eunice would give me a reflexology treatment using the finest aromatherapy oils. She prepared nutritious tasty meals using ingredients from her vegetable garden, supplemented with food from the nearby village market. Everything seemed so vibrant and full of vitality. Eunice also had two adorable dogs – Jack, a three-legged Jack Russell and Donna, the softest, most affectionate German Shepherd I'd ever met. Jack was a constant companion, mentoring me in the joy of living. Eunice's land included olive trees and scented shrubs which led to a swiftly running river, fed by mountain snow. As my energy increased, I would take the dogs for a woodland riverside walk each afternoon. Truly I'd found Paradise on Earth and had my very own guardian angel caring for me.

As I recharged and grew stronger, I could begin to hear my inner guidance again. After a month of this rejuvenating retreat, my next steps were now clear. I knew I had to leave London for Yorkshire to start a new life. But before I did that, I needed to have another smear test. Although I'd been travelling, I was still registered with my father's local GP. I was apprehensive about the test results, however for the first time in a few years my results came back normal. I was absolutely elated.

As soon as I found out, I rang Eunice. In between the blubbing of happy tears, I thanked her for all the loving care she had provided for me with such devotion and generosity. My cervical smear tests have been clear ever since. 12 years later I was able to have a natural menopause without needing a hysterectomy. I will always be forever grateful to the beautiful angel who heard my call to heal naturally and was there for me when I needed it most.

BERNIE DAVIES

Having held senior positions in top UK law firms and also running her own Practice for half her legal career, Bernie Davies is no stranger to the challenges that face business owners and managers. Davies has distinguished herself over the years by utilising effective networking and business development skills, which have earned her the respect of her peers as well as significant media interest. Author, Business Strategist, Mentor, Personal Brand Expert and sought-after speaker; Bernie has presented globally at several events including the United Nations, Geneva, Switzerland, the Caribbean and all across the United Kingdom. Bernie's passion is in helping people find the uniqueness in themselves and using that knowledge to create a winning personal and business brand!

www.Berniedavies.com

https://youtube.com/channel/UCEHg9TJhv2Shu4AzQTu86qg

https://twitter.com/bernieajackson

https://instagram.com/berniedaviesglobal/

https://facebook.com/berniedaviesglobal

Mind The Gap!

We have heard about selective listening, but I for one have been very guilty of selective story telling.

Not because I have any desire to deceive or mislead, but because I never had the courage before now to let people into my pain. And to be honest, I didn't really see the point. However, the older I get, the more I realise that my pain is my triumph and my hurt can heal others. So, I will re-tell my story of moving 236 miles from Bradford, West Yorkshire to Cardiff, Wales in 2006 by filling the gap between arriving here in June 2006 and becoming Head of Property at NewLaw Solicitors in October 2006. Why? Because those 5 months were some of the hardest months I have had. But in that gap, I found true strength.

Let's go back a year. It was 2005 and my soon to be husband (we got married the same July), took me to Chepstow, via Wales! I fell in-love with its lushness and beauty. That was it, no other place resonated with me in such an intense way except my birthplace, Jamaica! Now my Fiancé at the time was introduced to me by my son who felt I deserved happiness; he was the father of one of his friends. He apparently had an unfortunate past experience which made us a perfect match, as far as they were concerned! After much cajoling, I went on the first date and…. well you know the drill.

So fast forward 12 months and I acted upon my desire to move to Wales with the full backing of my family and husband. We miraculously got both our houses rented and moved to a furnished apartment in Penarth Marina, Cardiff. The whole process took a month. Leaving my adult sons in Bradford, we moved to Wales for an exciting new start for us and my 13 year old daughter.

Well, we all know that saying, "Man plans and God laughs!" Yes… that! Immediately upon launching into my new job at a prominent Cardiff city centre law firm, I was revisited with a vengeance by an age-old, ongoing female anomaly which had, for all intents and purposes, gone away. It resulted in me being hospitalised, bed ridden and told I would need to wait for an operation for at least a year. I found myself less than a month into starting a new job, incapable of fulfilling my work responsibilities and without any accrued sickness benefits. They naturally made a commercial decision and I was told it was not viable to keep me on. I did not make it past 6 weeks.

I should have realised something was amiss when my usually doting husband arrived at the hospital on the first occasion (I was rushed there straight from work), quite aloof. He refused to be with me when being examined or when the doctors were explaining the prognosis. It should have been even clearer when he started to say how long a day he had and that he hated sitting around in hospitals.

But as you know, we see what we want to see. I also did not see that every loan (except the mortgage on our house) was in my name only, including his new Mercedes Benz! It did not catch my attention that all my bank accounts had soon become joint. What is it they say about hindsight?

As you can probably imagine, worse was ahead. With July came the summer holidays and my daughter went off to Jamaica for summer camp and I was left in our rented apartment, on medically imposed bed rest. Without warning my husband moved out of the apartment, saying he'd had enough, took "OUR" money (yes I made it so by having a joint account) and left me with "MY" debts (yes that's also how it works).

I could not even have the satisfaction of reneging on his car loan as… wait for it… it must've been the only car loan in history that the car was NOT security for. So yes, I still had to pay for HIS car even though mine was paid in full. You can't make this up! And the icing on the cake is he left the country! All searches proved futile. This remained the case for more than 9 years!

You might be right in saying I brought it on myself being so trusting with someone I had only met a year before marrying. You would be right but what's the point? I was in deep, dire circumstances and I was ON MY OWN! The Church I attended at the time, as I always ensure I find a place to live out my faith in fellowship with likeminded people, didn't know what to do with me; bless them. They did their best by picking up ironing and dropping it back and other such helpful acts, but they just did not know what to say to me. So essentially loneliness became my friend for the first time in my entire life. I can tell you now that it is NO friend that anyone would want for dinner, let alone as a constant companion!

But I was running out of time and definitely out of money. Shame dictated that I kept it quiet. "What? Another failed marriage? You've got to be joking… NAH it's got to be her… can't keep a man, can she?" You know how it goes. So, I made myself THREE promises. The first was NOT to have another relationship until my daughter went to University. She was in year 9 so that meant minimum 5 years. The second, was to take a close look at myself and find out what's wrong with me (REAL TALK). The THIRD, and most important, was to get off my butt and make sh*t happen! It was up to me and I owed it to myself and my children.

Starting with the last and working backwards, I literally talked myself well. I had no choice! I could not afford to be ill. My daughter was returning in

September. She needed to be collected from Heathrow Airport (some 6 hours' drive both ways) and to come back to life almost as good as she left it. So, I pumped myself with prescribed hormone tablets to control the symptoms of my ongoing illness. As I knew I was NOT a candidate for a full-time job, I set about looking for locum positions. Oh, I almost forgot… I bought myself a satnav! Friendless, husbandless and in a strange city, you've got to admit that was the best buy ever!

It was a very dark time. I took locum positions in Bristol and then in Swindon; some 75 miles from home. Now you've got to put this in perspective. I am Jamaican. Despite always driving in Jamaica, I only got my UK license a year before then. Motorways were anathema to me. I drove nowhere without a satnav and even then, I was guaranteed to get lost. I once ended up on the way to London trying to get home from Leeds to Bradford! Therefore I quite sensibly decided to take public transport for my locum positions. I had to travel in the early hours, sometimes with 3 changes to get to work from Penarth Marina. I had to be all bright eyed and bubbly, overseeing AND motivating staff (I had only just met) on residential conveyancing transactions. It was NOT easy!

I would put on a brave face during the days and on the commute stare blankly out of the window, wondering whether those pretty little houses I was whooshing past held half the pain in them that my salubrious waterfront apartment concealed.

I would look out onto the passing boats with laughter ringing from them, wondering if I would ever truly laugh again. And when I threw my beautiful wedding set into the sea's depths, how I wished I could lose the hounding phone calls and the recurring worry along with them. But I could not allow myself the luxury of entertaining such thoughts for too long; I had to be strong. I had to 'feel the fear and do it anyway'.

Some days, the symptoms of my condition were exacerbated by the toll of the travel and stress and I had to manage it without letting on. I remember one night I missed my stop coming home and ended up getting off at the Dinas Powys stop, only 2 miles past my stop. Now if anyone knows Dinas Powys, it's really nowhere to be alarmed for your safety at 7pm. However, the stop is very quiet and secluded and I had visions of myself raped and murdered in the underbrush. I was in floods of tears and it wasn't the only time. The power of local knowledge was not mine at the time and so to me I was in the middle of an eerie slasher movie.

On another note, I discovered a doctor was my immediate neighbor and one day in the lift he asked after my husband. I'm sure he regretted it immediately. Out of embarrassment I believe, he said if anything ever happened, I should not hesitate to call him. It was more than a couple times thereafter he had to get me blue lighted to the hospital, in the middle of the night.

I soldiered on at the locum position in Swindon. My commute entailed me driving to Penarth station, getting the train to Cardiff Central, connecting through to Bristol Parkway, then another train to Swindon and finally a taxi to work; as no public transportation went there. And all this for an 8:30am start. Imagine that both ways each day, lonely and unwell with a debilitating illness. It took sheer grit and determination. I could not give up. I needed to keep my 'oxygen mask' on as my children needed me.

Interestingly, those two months working In Swindon turned out to be the happiest two months in a working environment that I can remember. For some reason, the team absolutely loved me. Quite incredibly, I managed to keep my spirits up. I was able to concentrate. I was able to build team rapport. And it went so well that I was actually offered a full-time position, with prospects of running the business in a few years as the then boss was up for retirement. The offer came with a great salary in excess of £60,000pa with relocation costs. I could not believe it.

How many of us know that the first shining bauble might not be for you? It's hard to struggle through tough times and harder still to resist the first 'solution' that presents itself. As incredible an offer as it was, and even more wonderful the team were that I was working with, I could not say yes. I had no other option, but I knew I could not move my daughter again. I had only just taken her from Bradford to Cardiff to a new school. She was only just adjusting to a new set of friends and a new environment. This could not be the answer... I was devastated, but I knew it was not for me.

Sometimes the answer you are looking for is just behind the counterfeit 'solution'. In that moment of deciding, you have to be confident at all times that if this is not the answer but it looks so incredibly wonderful, then the answer must be absolutely amazing and worth waiting for. So, I said thank you but no. I also asked the agent to keep trying, because I did feel somehow in my heart that the right job was there.

The other thing to bear in mind is, when you have finally found that answer there is no bright shining light. You can't hear the people cheering on the sidelines saying, "Yes, yes, yes! You've done it! Just a few more steps and you're there!" You simply have to continue with sometimes only a deep sense of knowing that you are heading in the right direction, that you made the right choice and that change will come.

Would you believe that immediately upon my refusing to take that offer I got the interview that changed everything?

So, in October 2006 when I took the job interview, walked into NewLaw solicitors and stepped into that boardroom with Helen Molyneux, I had no idea. I did not anticipate I was about to get the most amazing position with incredible opportunities propelling me through open doors that I would never have dreamed of. So from taking four different modes of transport to work I was now able (if I was fit enough) to walk across the Penarth Barrage to work. The longest route to work by car was now 15 minutes. I was able, in my lunch breaks, to walk across to the Millennium Centre and enjoy free daily concerts or dine in nearby restaurants. I met incredible people and was able to finally live the dream I envisioned when I took that journey in June 2006 from Bradford to Wales.

Looking back, I made three promises, didn't I? I'm pleased to say that I kept them all. I did not have a relationship until my daughter set me up on a dating site when she was in Upper Sixth Form. Anyone see the theme of kids playing cupid? Well, thankfully this one worked out because I did look into myself. I found out there was nothing wrong with me. What I discovered was there was something wrong with my 'picker'. I needed to change the way I decided and whom I decided to pick. Once I got that nailed, I was free to choose wisely and so I did. Today I'm married to Mark, with whom I have shared an incredible love and bond for 10 years.

I hope this small bit of my story helps to inspire hope and courage. Life is never going to be easy. Nothing lasts forever… even the good things end at some point. I found my strength in my belief in God and my sense of responsibility to my children. Whatever it is that drives you, when trouble comes, focus on it… set your face like a flint and, notwithstanding anything, never ever give up!

CHARLOTTE AVERY

Charlotte found writing this chapter very helpful in closing a chapter in her life. Having always worked in Finance, she believed that English was never her strong point, but this has proved that it isn't the case. Charlotte is currently looking at ways that will enable her to help other people going though similar situations and to help them discover what they really want from life. She continues to enjoy the single life, living in Croydon, South London.

charlotteavery57@gmail.com

https://instagram.com/char_avy_5

https://instagram.com/lovinlifeat40

https://facebook.com/charlotte.c.milner

What I've Always Wanted?

I never thought 20 years ago that at the age of 42 I would be single and living in the flat of my dreams. I always thought I'd be married with a couple of kids. I got together with my ex at the age of 25 and before that I had been in a six-year relationship since the age of 17. I had never really been on own, let alone living on my own. My ex and I got married in 2014, 11 years after we first started going out. We started living together quite early on in our relationship and bought our house in 2009. My husband was 14 years older than me but that never really mattered and when we got engaged it was a complete surprise to me. He arranged the ring and did it at Glastonbury Festival. I always wanted to get married, but he wasn't that keen. It didn't really bother me though as we had a very loving and, I thought, loyal relationship.

It was only 18 months after our wedding day that I found out he had been having an affair. I didn't believe it; all I knew was that I loved him. I forgave him and he said he wanted to work at our relationship, as he still loved me. Even to this day I am sure there was nothing wrong with our relationship; someone just caught his eye. It then took another 7 months before he moved out. During this time he continued to see her, but I convinced myself that it was going to be ok. We even went on a cruise for two weeks with my parents a month before we split up. I didn't speak to anyone about what was going on and even made up some mid -life crisis story for my best friend. I was breaking and hurting inside.

In August 2016, I finally got the courage and asked him to make the decision between me and her. He was away for a night and I told him I wanted to know the following day. Even then I was sure that he was going to pick me. I was so happy when he got home but he told me the news that was to change my life forever. It was over! It took him another two weeks to move out whilst I was away on holiday. On returning from the trip I had the task of telling my family and friends, who were deeply shocked and hurt. My parents and I decided not to tell my nan as we thought it would confuse her. This was something that I now regret as she will always see my life differently to what it is now.

The next few months were a blur, getting through each day as I could. I brought a few nice things for the house including a new bed, as I couldn't sleep in a bed which smelt of him! I also started divorce proceedings with the solicitor quite quickly after he left. That birthday/Christmas/New Year I kept myself busy and arranged to be away with family and friends.

In the February of the following year my nan unfortunately passed away at the grand age of 100 ¾s. She had been on her own for over 30 years and I admired her independence and spirit. I was struggling to come to terms with being on my own, having to pay the bills and generally having no one to lean on. At her funeral I cried my heart out, but as I walked behind her coffin on my own, I remember thinking if she could do it, I could too. That day I made a promise to her that I would.

That, I felt, was the first turning point in moving on from my marriage. I was turning 40 in the December so decided to do some of the things I had always wanted to do and start enjoying myself - and no one was going to stop me! I signed up to Tough Mudder and booked a singles holiday to Vietnam. I had a great summer that year; enjoying some gigs, dating (not looking for a relationship) and generally having a great time.

The divorce was going through and we had agreed our financial settlement. I finally got my Decree Absolute 1 week before I went to Vietnam in the October. That was a trip which changed my life. It was an amazing trip; we all got on so well and I made some friends for life. I felt I was finally being myself again. My 40th birthday came and went and I even spent New Year in on my own. I was getting used to my newly found freedom and was enjoying time spent by myself. It really was ok to be on your own.

I thought I was dealing with everything really well, but in March 2018 I found I was actually struggling to process what was going on. I started counselling sessions, something my boss had suggested to me. I'd never really thought about it, but she could obviously see something wasn't quite right. I was having a bad time at work and what I was experiencing outside of work was having an impact.

One of the things that I discovered during my counselling sessions was how I didn't tell my parents things as I was worried how they would react. My dad had bought me a mug for the previous Christmas saying, 'I am really busy' as a joke, but he said it was because I always said it to them. One of the things I have started to do is talk to them more, tell them how I feel and what I am doing. This has certainly improved my relationship with my parents and I believe helped them understand more about what I am about. I now talk to them more than ever!

That June I went on another amazing holiday to Peru. I climbed Rainbow Mountain and the steps up to Machu Picchu and I came back from the holiday feeling like I could achieve anything, feeling so free. During that holiday I made the decision to sell my house as it didn't feel like my home anymore. I also wanted to change my job; actually, I wanted to change my whole life!

A month after coming back from Peru I was signed off work for stress. A colleague at work had sat me down and asked me if I was ok, which I obviously wasn't. I clearly remember walking into the doctor's the following morning and explaining how I was feeling, or trying to. I felt very relieved when I was signed off knowing I didn't have to go to work. I slowly started to make the house look nice, control my eating and had a few days in a health spa. It was all about the self-care. It felt like I was actually starting to process my divorce and being off work gave me the space to do that.

I was very fortunate during this time that my friend Donna (who I'd met in Vietnam) was quitting her job and planning to go travelling round Australia. I had already booked flights to go and see her after the Christmas and New Year period, so I cancelled them and booked a one-way ticket to travel out there just before Christmas. This also gave me a good reason to sell the house before then. For the next few months that was all I focused on. Thankfully I sold the house, moving out 2 days before flying to Australia. With my life either in storage or in a suitcase, who knew what was going to happen next!

I was lucky enough to have the holiday of a lifetime in Australia and this enabled me to get to grips with what had happened over the last 2 years. On my last evening of that holiday, I made a video and even wrote a text to my ex, telling him all the things I had ever wanted to. I never sent it. Divorce has not put me off marrying again but I was very surprised by what a huge impact it has had on my life. My best advice I can give someone going through a similar situation is to just give yourself space and time to deal with it and learn to love yourself. It is ok to be on your own. I am now 42, single and working through sorting out other areas of my life, but that would be another few chapters! I am enjoying the freedom of having no commitments, which I think some people are jealous of. I am the happiest I have ever been and looking forward to what the future holds.

CHLOE LLOYD

Hey, I'm Chloe and I am 21. I am currently working as an Outreach Support Worker for Headway Bristol, which is a charity that supports adults with brain injuries and assists them to live independently. I decided to write my chapter as my dad had written one in a Discover Your Bounce book previously and I mentioned to him how it would be a good idea for a book from the family's points of view. He then introduced me to the team and said I should get involved and here I am writing this!

Take A Deep Breath

It all started when I was 13 years old. My dad was taken to hospital on January 1st 2013 with a spontaneous midline cerebellar haemorrhage (caused when a blood vessel is blocked or bleeding, causing an interruption to part of the brain called the cerebellum). He then contracted kidney disease, adrenal insufficiency and two brain conditions called hydrocephalus and ventriculitis. Hydrocephalus is the build up of fluid in the ventricles deep in the brain which causes pressure on the brain. Ventriculitis is the inflammation on the ependymal lining of the cerebral ventricles which is an infection similar to meningitis. This went on for a total of six months from admission to being discharged from rehabilitation at the end of June.

Most of those six months are a complete blur to me. I'm assuming my brain has blocked it out because this was the hardest time of my life so far. I was unsure if I was going to get my dad back at the end or if I was going to have to say goodbye. I would prepare myself every night in bed for if that was to happen. There were many times we would think he was recovering and then he'd go downhill; it really was a rollercoaster.

Being 13 is a hard age for any kid. You're preparing to pick your choices for your GCSE's, developing into a teenager so your hormones are all over the place and trying to juggle a social life. At this time I was very sensitive; every little thing got to me and made me emotional. For example, one morning before school I remember falling out with my mum over something so silly and I ran round to my friend's house sobbing. I gave her and her poor mum a heart attack as they understandably instantly thought something had gone wrong with my dad.

I was what some would call 'bullied' in school. I don't like to use that term because labelling people for something that happened as kids seems harsh to me; I no longer know what they are like now as people. I'd spend the majority of my school days with my head down, walking from class to class with my friends, being verbally abused down the hallways. At first this really troubled me; I would kick and scream about attending school in the mornings. Getting home from school, I would sit and cry to my mum most days about moving schools. I never did end up moving schools, but I am glad as I think the experience really helped strengthen who I am.

By the time I turned 15 I was still being verbally abused, but I had become immune to it. I would no longer hear their harsh words and be unaware they were even saying anything to me until someone would say, "Can't you hear that?" to which I'd just smile and shrug.

Personally, I think the school could have handled it all much better as I wasn't really supported throughout this time. They offered me time to sit alone in a room to do my work if I was feeling upset, but that wasn't going to help me as I was and still am a huge over-thinker. I over-think myself into bad moods by making up scenarios in my head that aren't true, but could be possible, and make myself worry about them for days.

School's advice would be 'stay away from them,' which was impossible considering I had lessons with them. My friends and I would often sit to eat our lunch under staircases, in classrooms and mini corridors to avoid bumping into them during break times so that we could enjoy ourselves. I often felt guilty as they'd be brought into the experience and be verbally abused too. I'd blame myself for it because they were my friends.

Around this time there was a site called ask.fm where you could leave anonymous comments on people's pages; it was really toxic. I would often get told to die, or that I should harm myself, and many comments about my relationship with my boyfriend, who I'm still with now. I used to really beat myself up about it at one stage. I didn't dare tell my family about the site as they'd tell me to delete it, but I wanted to be the same as everybody else. Now I realise maybe I kept it as it was feeding me things I thought were true about myself and clarifying it for me.

Although it was bad, aside from that I loved school. I had a lot of fun with my friends that year; I would go to parties - sometimes getting ready for them in the hospital to spend more time with my dad. I also started seeing my current boyfriend, who I spoke about before, during this time. I remember feeling guilty about being happy and wanting to spend time with him and my friends, knowing that my dad was stuck in the hospital bed not able to even sit out at one stage. My family were all very supportive, they pushed me to keep going and get out there. They would say it's the start of my teenage years, I didn't want to waste them. It felt good to know they were happy for me to be happy, as I often worried they'd think of me as being selfish.

I've always been shy around new people and would get anxious before social events (I still do occasionally). I have never been to see anybody about my mental health. I was advised to due to everything that had happened to me, but I always felt it would show weakness in me. Now at 21 I feel it would have helped me hugely during this time and that there is nothing to be ashamed of. It shows a strong person to be able to go and seek help for their mental health and to be able to speak about it with somebody. I now know I have the option to consider if I do ever feel myself slipping back into that bad mindset.

Currently I am happy. I have a good relationship with my family, including my dad who I see as often as possible. We often go for coffee dates, which seems to be our favourite meeting point. I have the best group of friends around me; always supporting everything I do and helping to guide me. I now have a job which I have been in for a year already! I'm really settled in and enjoying the work. I love having a job that makes me feel like I have a purpose and am doing something beneficial. Helping others makes me feel good, which also helps with bad days because it makes me feel like I've helped somebody else to have a good day; even if it is just a catch up with them when they're feeling down. I like that I can relate to many of them and their families' situations.

Of course, I still have rough days where I don't want to get out of bed and shy away from the world, but those days aren't as often anymore. To help me with those days, I try to keep busy and push myself to do something I enjoy or something productive, so that I don't feel a day is wasted. Whether it be watching my favourite TV shows or meeting with friends.

A quote I find helpful on those days is: "Take a deep breath, it's just a bad day not a bad life."

Chloe X

EMMA JAY

Emma is a Lifestyle Coach. After years of stress and depression, she now helps stressed out professionals to regain control over their health and happiness. Emma believes in living in moderation and finding a routine that suits us as individuals; something that enables us to be the best version of ourselves. This ensures we are fit and healthy enough to give our loved ones the best of us too.

Stress can kill health and happiness. Emma's passion is to move people away from this destructive state and instead, into a thriving lifestyle by understanding their mind and body more, to take back control.

www.emmajlifeshaper.com

https://uk.linkedin.com/in/emma-j-00800652

https://facebook.com/emmajlifeshaper/

https://instagram.com/emmajlifeshaper/

https://twitter.com/Emmajlifeshaper

From Success To The Gutter And Back Again

At 23 years old I already had a very successful and full life. I was a sales manager in a very large company, earning more money than I ever thought possible at that age. In fact, too much money. I didn't know what to do with it, other than waste it on designer clothes and partying. I had bought my own home at 21, having no real understanding of money, and I kept up my expensive party girl lifestyle in the best clothes; spending every penny I earnt.

I loved the gym and had always kept fit since being a child; competing at athletics and horse riding for my county and country. I loved life; I was fun, loud, happy, positive and very ambitious. I was a finalist in a modelling competition and was signed by the agency to do work with them. I also danced for a promotions company in big live events. Dancing had been a passion of mine for many years and I loved getting paid for doing something I enjoyed.

Maybe I shouldn't have been surprised, but the company I worked for went into liquidation and closed when I had only been living in my house a few months. Shortly after, I nearly lost my house and was forced to sell it. This left me in huge debt and back living with my mum, miles away from my friends and the life I had built over the past few years.

When looking for a new job, there was nothing at all with a wage anywhere near what I had been used to. I felt my life slipping away beneath me. I got credit cards and loans to support my lifestyle and got into trouble financially.

The life that I had known felt like a fictional film that I had seen, not something I really lived. This was just the beginning of my downward spiral from success to the gutter.

I've since learnt that when things start going wrong in your life, it's like a domino effect of negatives; one after another. This was exactly what was about to happen to me.

Moving back with my mum meant that I got mixed up with the wrong crowd, which left me very insecure and settling for a life that I felt was all I could get and all I deserved at that point.

I was struggling to find a job, but mainly due to my pig headedness of chasing the dream job that I'd once had, which in all honesty didn't exist now. I flitted from sales company to sales company, just covering my 'going out' money and I turned into a not very nice person due to the negative influence others were having on me. I was lost, vulnerable and confused.

While looking for a job, I accepted a door to door sales role with a friend's boss. I hadn't even been there for 2 weeks when I was driving home and got hit from behind by another car; I remember it to this day. The weather wasn't very nice that day, with drizzly rain which is horrible to drive in.

I was stopped behind traffic on a steep hill and I guess the guy behind me didn't brake in time. He hit me, then I went into the car in front of me. I was in a borrowed Ford Fiesta at the time. I can remember being thrust up out of my seat and, with a severe thud, hit my forehead on the solid metal bar around the windscreen.

It was the worst pain I had ever experienced, just like someone had taken a knife and stabbed me. I looked in the mirror and all I could see was a hole in my head and what could only have been my skull. The next thing, blood squirted out in all directions - even from my nose. I reached into the back of the car and got an oily jumper of my friend's to hold on the wound to try and stop the blood.

The road I was on was quite busy; I can remember climbing into the passenger seat to open the door onto the grass at the side of the road. The man had got out of the car behind me and was standing about 10 feet away; grey, shaking and clearly in shock with the sight of so much blood. I shouted for him to call an ambulance and that's all I can remember until I woke up in one.

I had 15 stitches in what I can only describe as a Nike tick shaped laceration in my head. I had whiplash and the biggest rugby ball shaped lump, like I was growing another head.

As you can imagine my life flashed before my eyes. Before this, the only things I felt I had left was the future modelling contracts and my dancing, both of which I felt I could never do again with a huge scar on my face.

The scar on my face wasn't the only thing that car accident left me with. I had severe migraines, sickness and blackouts from the head injury. This was so frightening, as I couldn't go out on my own or drive.

It took me a while to realise, but I suffered depression as well, not even wanting to leave my bedroom most days. Instead of my nice clothes, I had given in to baggy tracksuits and what I had always called 'scruffs'.

I did zero exercise. The few times I tried to go back to the gym when I was eventually driving again, I would see a full car park, have raging anxiety, turn my car around and go home. I had lost all of my confidence and felt so insecure and paranoid in public.

I was a shadow of myself and struggled to remember my life as it was, with my nice car, expensive clothes, high flying job and loving my social life.

I was 24 and felt my life may as well be over.

I felt like I was in a deep dark hole, with absolutely no way out and no one to help me.

On top of all this, we lost my nan who was a massive part of my life.

The domino effect just kept going and I didn't know why all of this was happening to me, what had I done to deserve this? Self-pity, self-doubt and massive insecurities plagued me every day.

I had been handed a bag full of antidepressants from the doctor, but no other help whatsoever. I was just left to deal with all that had happened to me; no guidance, no support and honestly no consideration for my mental well-being.

I got home and my mum, who is a nurse, immediately put the tablets in the bin; she didn't want me to take them. I agreed with this, but I had no idea how I was going to get better.

My mum's partner (my now-step dad) was living with us too and as much as we had always got on, having lived over 30 minutes away and having a very busy life, we never really had time to bond, until now.

My step dad had suffered from depression for years and so he was the only one right then who understood what I was going through.

I remember it like it was yesterday; he set me small tasks to complete every day. I had a list on the back of my bedroom door with the basics on:

Get up by 8am.

Wash face, clean teeth, get dressed.

Go downstairs, have breakfast.

By 9am I would sit at his desk and do some admin work for him and he would check in with me every hour until 1pm, when I would then have lunch and probably go back to bed again.

This may seem basic to many of you, but this list, these basic tasks daily and the accountability to him, saved my life. We would then chat each day about who I now wanted to be, what did I enjoy, what did I want to do, what made me happy.

I remembered my love for exercise and how good it made me feel; how strong, fit and healthy I was when I was exercising daily and I wanted to feel that way again. So, my mum and step dad lent me money to do some courses; Gym Instructor, nutrition diplomas and then from there I found a passion again. This was something that excited me; something that made me want to get up, get dressed and smile again.

I did course after course and finally decided I wanted to help people who had suffered like I had.

I was young and slim and yet I still felt insecure, lacked confidence and found it very difficult to enter a gym environment. If I felt this way, then how did older ladies, larger ladies, ladies who also suffered with anxiety and depression feel?

I wanted to create a safe, happy, positive, supportive environment for any woman to come and get fitter, happier and healthier; with no judgment, just complete love and support. So, my mum and I decided to become partners. She would stay in her job; I would give mine up and put all of my time into our ladies-only gym and we would see how it would go.

Well, it boomed straight away. There was nothing like it in our area and my mum and I made amazing partners. She had her medical background and retrained as a yoga instructor and decided to become a personal trainer. She learnt a lot more about nutrition, hormones and mindset. I became a life coach to understand more about the mind, people's behaviours and choices and we created something very special.

The accident changed my life, which at the time I felt I couldn't recover from.

I now look back and see that the accident actually changed my life for the better. The life I had lived for the few years previously had to end. I had to stop, grow up and take responsibility. I learnt so much about me - the real me. How strong I am, what I want from life, all I'm capable of and most importantly my purpose in life.

Since then I have changed hundreds of lives with my coaching. I have spoken and performed on stage, had a lifestyle tv show on a local tv station, spoken weekly on a local radio station and been nominated and won awards for helping others.

Life has a strange way of showing us where we need to be, but when it does – wow! We can really thrive.

GIFTY ENRIGHT

Gifty Enright is an Author, International Speaker, Coach and Thought Leader specialising in Women and Workplace Wellbeing. Her book, Octopus on a Treadmill: Women, Success, Health, Happiness, has been widely praised, including by Joanna Lumley OBE. She has addressed Women's Networks at Wells Fargo Bank, Oxford University, Citi Bank, IBM, BP, and Tedx Women to name a few.

Born in Kumasi, Ghana, Gifty has lived for the past 30 years in Hertfordshire, UK and is married with two children.

www.giftyenright.com

https://linkedin.com/in/giftyenright/

https://facebook.com/giftyenright/

https://instagram.com/gifty.enright/

https://twitter.com/Gifty_Enright

Whose Life Is It Anyway?

I had taken six months maternity leave for my first baby and everything went swimmingly until the day I was due to go back to work. The baby, who was now mobile, decided it was the best day to fall off the bed! After six months off I couldn't phone in and say, "I forgot to have eyes in the back of my head and as a consequence my baby fell off the bed and now I'm taking him to see the doctor in case he has a brain injury." I left him with my mother and a long list of instructions. I was still breastfeeding at this point and in my panic to get to work on time, I forgot to use my breast pads. Lunchtime found me in the toilets fashioning breast pads out of toilet roll and wondering how long they would last before I started leaking into my top. After breast pad watch, repeated calls to my mum and a day of meetings, I was exhausted – both physically and mentally. I felt completely overwhelmed and it was only Monday!

This was the blueprint of my life. High powered job, a busy family – I felt like an octopus on a treadmill.

Crunch time

"How are you, Gifty?" the doctor asked.

His question was well meaning, but it left me confused. Why was he asking me how I was? I had brought my baby to his surgery for a routine check-up. My mother was in tow to enquire about some age-related ailment or another. *I* wasn't on the agenda. OK, there was, of course, that small matter of me having recently undergone double major surgery; one procedure to remove my appendix and the other to go in to my abdomen to explore why it had become distended with fluid. I had given birth with no pain killers just a few days before the major surgery. Despite this, I never put myself on the agenda at all.

It was a good question, as a few years after the birth of my second child I found myself at a Harley Street Clinic presenting the doctor with a spreadsheet of 14 'women's symptoms':

Night sweats

Achy joints

Foggy brain

Memory issues

Heart palpitations

Sore breasts

Anxiety / mood swings

Headaches

No libido

Heavy periods

Irregular periods

Urinary tract infections

Digestives issues

Extreme tiredness

I was at Harley Street seeing a private doctor because, as usual with the NHS, you have to literally walk into the doctors' surgery holding your uterus in your hands to be taken seriously. After a few appointments I felt I was getting nowhere because I was being told that my symptoms were consistent with my age, blah blah blah… I decided to take my life in my own hands and go private. Plus, my husband was fed up with my whingeing.

Picture this: following my consultation with one of the leading gynaecologists in Harley Street, I'm walking towards Great Portland Street tube station in London, completely stunned out of my wits, clutching HRT at the grand old age of 44! Wasn't life supposed to start at 40? Well I was only four years into that, so what was I doing clutching HR f*cking T? To add insult to injury, I'd had a scan and the consultant was surprised that my bone density was less than ideal. Apart from the fact that my eyeballs were revolving in my head by the unwelcome reality that I was facing, I was now being told that there was something wrong with my bone density. By the time I got back to Great Portland Street tube station I had developed a limp. I had been fine that morning. Ok, I had 14 symptoms, but I sure as hell wasn't limping. There had been no pain in my hip, so how did I suddenly develop this hip pain after hearing about less than ideal bone density? How did I end up here?

That's was when I knew something had to give. I just couldn't continue the life I was living. I was trying to have it all, but it was costing me my health. My hope is that I can pass on the lessons I have learnt so that you don't find yourself standing by a tube station questioning your bone density and your sanity.

From realisation to action

I started with getting to know myself. Understanding my hormone cycle, paying attention to the food I was eating and doing a lot of research! In fact, so much research that in 2018 I wrote a book which I called 'Octopus on a Treadmill' as it described how my life had been and what I had learned.

My research led me to understand that we need balance across the physical, mental, emotional and spiritual areas of our lives. We need to understand what they mean to us and to take action to bring each area back into balance. A lot of us live one-sided lives and don't understand that our life systems are interconnected, that to get the best out of life you have to look at things holistically. You have to evaluate yourself and your body and consider what you put into your body, how you work, how you play and how you rest. This needs to be underpinned by a resilient mindset which is made of the mental, emotional and spiritual. That is how you get to release the Goddess within.

Change is hard and you need to be anchored in something to power your change and that is where spiritual framework comes in. Spirituality gives you context and purpose. Spirituality is your connection to yourself, your community and to a higher source. There are a lot of people who feel lost, have no sense of purpose and feel their lives don't matter, so they don't fight as hard for the life that they deserve. You need to find that special connection and anchor that spirituality gives and from that point you will be practically unstoppable to achieve any change that you want in your life.

As I researched and learned, I applied the lessons to my life. I turned to meditation, exercise, wholefoods and paying attention to my self-talk and releasing toxic emotions. I now share my learning with others. I run workshops which are small and intimate and a bit like a grown-up pyjama party, only you learn life skills to help you live authentically and in balance. I also run coaching programmes to show you how to avoid the pitfalls and live well.

My conclusion

Women are pivotal to society. We have to make sure we are valued for what we bring to the table. To do this we have to value and take care of ourselves. We are still fighting a few battles on several fronts to get the recognition we deserve and until that happens, and I am optimistic enough to believe equal opportunities will happen, we owe it to ourselves to live our best lives.

That life should not be back to front. You need to set your lens, your template, whatever you choose to call it, and that lens should be set by your values and purpose. Your values should be what brings you joy and aligns with your purpose. What do you think you were put on this earth for? What makes your heart sing? What does a good life look like for you?

For those of you thinking, "What are my values?" They should cover:

Physical

Mental

Emotional

Spiritual

Our lives are complex; we all have challenges to face. Rather than facing life from a deficit and being reliant on coffee and prescription drugs to power us through, while feeling semi-detached from our reality, we know enough now to take care of ourselves. We therefore have a fighting chance of bringing out the best in ourselves in the way we are designed to be. It's exquisite!

HOLLY PROSSER

Holly is an enthusiastic entrepreneur, charity committee member, Human Resources professional and beautician living in Gloucestershire. Her first passion lies in listening to people, whether that be the business owners or employees she works with, or those that take a seat in her brow and lash chair for an hour of pampering and off-loading. Her second passion is that of making people feel valued. Finding herself as a 20-something woman questioning her sexuality in a strange world focused on stereotypes and perfectionism, Holly uncovered a true love for empowering inclusivity.

Always looking to grow, both personally and professionally, Holly decided to tick off one of the '30 things to do before I'm 30' bucket list, and put her English Literature degree to good use in this chapter.

https://linkedin.com/in/holly-prosser-hrstar

Sign On The Dotted Line

"Can you sign on the dotted line?"

This wasn't the postman asking me to sign for my usual online clothes order that I'd then try and hide from my mum's beady eyes.

Nor for some tickets to the next gig of my favourite artist.

I was being asked to sign in agreement for my consultant to take away my ovary and fallopian tube.

Not what anyone expects to be asked a week before their 23rd birthday, right?

Throughout my teen years, I had always suffered immensely with my periods. As a petite, slim and under-developed 12-year-old, I didn't expect to start my period before most of my friends. I remember the day, shamefully talking to my best friend whilst burying my head in my locker, "This is so embarrassing! What's happening to me?" I'm sure most girls and women alike can relate. Familiarising myself with 'feminine hygiene' products to get me through it was just as daunting – feeling like you're wearing a nappy whilst trying to fit in with the 'cool girls' at school wasn't ideal.

Little did I know I'd soon become familiar with pain too - lots of it.

Awakening in the middle of the night with horrific cramps, not being able to sit down comfortably, and the tightening of my school skirt around a now prominently bloated belly. The pain wasn't just in my stomach either, it was down my thighs and in my lower back. It was unbearable and soon stopped me from enjoying even the small things in life.

And the period cramps were just the start.

It triggered migraines, sickness and even Irritable Bowel Syndrome. My body felt like it wasn't my own anymore. I was by no means in control of it; instead, it overpowered me and dominated my every move. Do I feel ok to go to a friend's for dinner? How am I going to wear a leotard for my next dance class? I hope the teacher will let me take another loo break! I felt ashamed, embarrassed, and constantly on edge.

Despite the overwhelming fear of how my body would make me feel on a day to day basis, I rarely allowed others to see how it was affecting me. After all, I just assumed this was what being a female meant, right? I was one of the unfortunate ones, one to suffer badly with what mother nature throws at us monthly, there was nothing more to it.

But after years of suffering with the pain, and side effects becoming more and more frequent, a trip to the doctor was my only option. I felt silly. "It's just a period!" I'd tell my mum. "I just need to take some paracetamol and get on with it!" I'd try and convince myself just of that - that I could 'get on with it' - but I knew deep down that something wasn't right.

After multiple doctors' appointments, hospital trips and gastroenterology tests, I was still nowhere closer to a true diagnosis or treatment. Being told numerous times, 'it's just irritable bowel syndrome', 'take some Buscopan', was frustrating and fed my belief that I was just being over dramatic.

Until one day, the pain hit like a tonne of bricks. The ache in my stomach, the burning in my back and the stabbing pain in my cervix. My mum rushed me straight to my doctors, where I saw a female GP who took one look at me and said, "I'm referring you to gynaecology," and prescribed me some painkillers to help manage the pain.

Finally, someone got it. I wasn't just a young girl who couldn't cope with a bit of pain, I was in genuine need of some help and a diagnosis to help me manage whatever was going on with my body.

Weeks and months passed, and whilst the pain relief helped, it couldn't be a long-term solution. I met with my new consultant and we discussed my history. He suggested I should have a laparoscopy (key-hole surgery) to look for Endometriosis.

En-doh-me-tree-oh-sis.

It swirled around in my head after my appointment and I was straight on to Google, researching what this strange word even meant. "There's only 1 in 3 chance that you'll have it, but we will check anyway," my consultant had reassured me. I must have only been in the room for 10 minutes, if that, and he seemed pretty sure that it probably wouldn't be the case, but I was still intrigued.

Everyone says not to self-diagnose on Google, right? But the NHS website must be a reliable source of information, I thought to myself.

"Endometriosis is a condition where tissue similar to the lining of the womb starts to grow in other places, such as the ovaries and fallopian tubes.

Endometriosis can affect women of any age.

It's a long-term condition that can have a significant impact on your life, but there are treatments that can help."

Talk of 'tissue' and 'womb' was unnerving, but what made me even more anxious was the similarities in my symptoms, with that of endometriosis:

"Pain in your lower tummy or back (pelvic pain) – usually worse during your period

Period pain that stops you doing your normal activities

Pain during or after sex

Pain when peeing or pooing during your period

Feeling sick, constipation, diarrhoea, or blood in your pee during your period

Difficulty getting pregnant"

I reminded myself how relaxed my consultant seemed, almost certain that it wouldn't be what I have.

After one cancelled date for my laparoscopy (much to my annoyance) and over 6 months since I was referred, I finally had the laparoscopy I had been waiting for. I hadn't had an operation since I was 4 years old when I had my tonsils removed, but I was ready for it. I just wanted some clarity, even if it was to rule Endometriosis out.

After the operation, I awoke, hazy, with a throat as dry as the Sahara Desert.

The consultant came into my room, still in his relaxed manner, and said, "The operation went well!"

I felt relieved.

"You do have Endometriosis, significantly on your left side, on your cervix, in your Pouch of Douglas and some on your right-hand side. There was too much there for us to remove during this operation, so we'll schedule another routine laparoscopy to remove what's there and look at managing your symptoms with different birth control. I'll follow-up with you in clinic."

I was confused, dazed, perplexed. Pouch of Douglas? Cervix? Too much? I thought he said the operation went well! Was I still sleepy from the anaesthetic and not hearing him correctly? Was this a good thing? To finally have a diagnosis, some clarification that I wasn't in pain for no reason, it wasn't just IBS or a 'bad period'. But what did this mean for me?

I soon came to learn that my consultant was usually relaxed in his manner. I do sometimes wonder how a male consultant can really understand what a diagnosis like this can feel like for a woman. I'd always dreamed of having a family. When I was practically a baby myself, I couldn't wait to have babies. Always playing with baby Annabel and gazing lovingly at the new babies born on my cul-de-sac. I couldn't wait for it to be me; it was like my destiny. Had this chance now been ripped away from me?

My follow-up clinic appointment went through my stage-two diagnosis in more detail and my consultant suggested that a coil could be fitted during the operation to manage the growth of Endometriosis in the future. This was a chronic condition, not easily diagnosed, typically only through a laparoscopy; which like any operation, brings its own dangers. Although my consultant could remove what endometrial tissue was there, we could not be sure how long it would keep away. To have the coil fitted and hopefully lessen, or even stop, my periods was the only way we could try and keep it at bay. My fertility was intact for now, but I still had a long road of uncertainty ahead of me whilst managing this invisible disease.

I recovered quickly from my second operation, but only a year later was torn down once again when my doctor found a large cyst on my ovary. This made my condition all the more real. My consultant's once 'relaxed' manner was now a little more serious, which ignited a fear in me. He'd made it clear that the NHS waiting list to have the cyst removed, which was growing rapidly, was 9-12 months, by which time it was likely to burst and destroy my ovary along with it. I'd be rushed into an emergency operation and would be left with a big scar to show for it. Not a clean, tidy job like the key-hole surgery I knew.

This petrified me.

But thankfully, I had private healthcare and was seen within 6 weeks.

Almost exactly 2 years since my first operation I was back again, signing on the dotted line; this time with real fear and anxiety that things could look much different on the other side of this operation.

"Sign here." The nurse pointed, speaking in a comforting tone.

I was signing to agree to have my ovary and fallopian tube removed if the cyst and fluid compromised their condition. There was something about the thought of this that made me feel less womanly if I were to only have one ovary. At not even 23 this was terrifying, but I knew it needed to be done and after a couple of years of coming to terms with my condition, and being grateful for how far I'd already come, I placed my fate and my future in the hands of the nurses, doctors and the universe.

C'est la vie.

What will be, will be. If I'm meant to have babies, if I'm meant to be a mum, the universe will make it happen.

And just like that, I was given yet another chance, another glimmer of hope that my dreams are aligned with the universe.

Despite the anaesthetic still in my system, I almost immediately awoke and asked the nurse what the outcome was as soon as I could.

She told me that my consultant had re-constructed my ovary and my fallopian tube was left unscathed.

I have never felt relief and gratitude like it. For once, it was good news! I still had both ovaries, both fallopian tubes, all in good condition. The recovery from this operation was much more difficult and I was sore for quite some weeks after, however I felt like my dreams of a family were still in reach, like I'd gained some control back over my body. Holly: 1, Endometriosis: 0.

Now I just take each day as it comes. I still have days where the pain creeps back in and I'm reminded that my condition is chronic, but my overall health is much better and I have been able to enjoy life, travel, see the world and be young! I count my blessings and feel grateful for the world we live in, the people who surround me and my overall good health.

If it's meant to happen, believe that the universe will bring it to you.

JULES HELENS

Jules is a retired nurse now running her own Bristol-based business. She works with women as a Wellbeing Life Coach focusing on health, happiness and the menopause journey. Jules inspires and motivates women to connect with and rebalance their head, heart and body. She achieves this by helping them to become unstuck mentally, emotionally and physically so they can find their way to living and embracing a healthier and happier life.

Jules has designed a Wellbeing Life Coaching programme based on the tools and techniques used in Cognitive Behavioural Therapy and positive psychology's model of wellbeing. This bespoke, step-by-step programme takes women on a journey of self-discovery and enables them to unlock positive long-lasting changes so they can enhance their overall sense of wellbeing.

www.wellbeinglife.co.uk

https://facebook.com/JulesHellensWLC

https://instagram.com/wellbeinglifecoach

https:// linkedin.com/in/jules-hellens/

https:// youtube.com/channel/UCXKymVl1GKkdWHvzEZZdMHw

My Menopause Journey: Mayhem To Magnificence

The menopause is a much-talked-about subject now, but ten years ago it was a taboo subject. Consequently, when I first started to transition into the early stages of the menopause I was not prepared mentally, emotionally or physically for what was about to happen to me. Owing to the lack of information, numerous myths and lots of assumptions and ignorance on my part, I found my initial journey through the menopause challenging. This had a negative impact on my wellbeing – but it doesn't have to be that way!

Going through the menopause doesn't have to be debilitating or diminishing for any woman. It's very much a natural part of ageing and a great opportunity to take stock of what is or isn't working in our lives. So, I thought I would share my menopause journey with you and how I went from mayhem to magnificence.

My childhood years were very happy. I had a great relationship with my mum, so when I became a young teenager, my mum talked to me about periods. She prepared me practically and emotionally. I wasn't traumatised when it eventually happened because I had been informed; I knew exactly what to expect.

My mum also told me that, one day, my periods would stop. This was called 'the menopause' or 'going through the change'. She told me that she hadn't experienced any symptoms, so I didn't think much more of it. In my twenties and early thirties, I was living a life of new experiences that brought their challenges, but I was happy. I was having regular periods, where I felt a bit rubbish each month with premenstrual tension, but the impact on my life was minimal.

In my late thirties, I started to consider the menopause. I observed work colleagues and friends of a certain age fanning themselves or quickly taking off their jumper even though the room was cold. Apart from hot flushes, I didn't really know much more about the menopause. No one discussed it and I didn't ask. I happily went through life thinking nothing more of it.

In my mid-forties, things started to change. I would get what I thought were urinary tract infections (symptom 1). My GP took urine samples. The results were negative, but he gave me antibiotics anyway. Then my periods started to go a bit haywire (symptom 2). My GP told me to take a pregnancy test. It was negative – thank goodness! I really didn't want to start a family at the age of 49. I became forgetful with terrible brain fog (symptom 3), I couldn't concentrate (symptom 4), I had an overwhelming feeling of fatigue (symptom 5) and I lost motivation for the things I loved doing the most (symptom 6).

At this point, not one GP mentioned that I might be perimenopausal. Maybe it was because I was still having periods and it hadn't occurred to them. It most definitely hadn't occurred to me – at this point in my journey, I had never even heard of the term 'perimenopause'. Then, in my early fifties, my periods stopped altogether. Now, the night sweats started (symptom 7), I couldn't sleep (symptom 8), I experienced loss of libido and vaginal atrophy (symptoms 9 and 10), I had 15+ hot flushes a day, which triggered anxiety and panic attacks (symptoms 11 and 12 and 13), I became irritable and irrational (symptoms 14 and 15). There are approximately 34 symptoms of the menopause and each woman will experience some or none of these symptoms. For me, the 15 symptoms I experienced were debilitating.

While the physical symptoms were difficult, the most challenging aspect was the mental side of the menopause. Overnight, I became a gibbering wreck and everything around me felt like mayhem. Worst of all, I had no idea what was happening – it was scary. I hadn't suffered from anxiety or panic attacks at any time in my life, so it was a shock to experience them now. With no previous experiences, I hadn't developed any coping strategies for the way I was feeling.

It was like a light had gone out and the things that made me me had gone. I felt lost and stuck in a rut, which had a negative impact on my overall sense of wellbeing. I was desperate. I started to question this new way of feeling and googled my symptoms. I discovered the term 'perimenopause' and my symptoms fitted. Luckily, I have a super-supportive husband and together we looked at natural treatments.

I tried every herbal remedy on offer, but nothing worked. I saw a nutritionist and changed my diet. I started taking targeted multivitamins for the menopause. I continued to exercise, which included strength work in the gym and Pilates, but nothing was helping to relieve my symptoms fast enough for me. I started to research the menopause further and discovered that there was a lack of understanding not just by women, but also by the medical professionals – I was not alone. I googled HRT (Hormone Replacement Therapy), and armed with information and determination, went to another GP. I was lucky this time. This GP was well informed and gave me the time and space to go through the risks and benefits of taking HRT. I made a choice and decided to try it.

Within two weeks, I was back to being me. I regained my overall sense of wellbeing mentally, physically and emotionally. I had my life back – and my husband had his wife back! While I was taking HRT, I felt able to make further lifestyle changes. I took up meditation, I practised mindfulness and I started a daily gratitude journal. I limited my intake of coffee, sugar and carbohydrates, and reduced my alcohol consumption (I even managed one year alcohol-free).

I started tennis lessons, I completed an MSc in Business Management, I gave up my nursing career and I retrained as a Wellbeing Life Coach, focusing on health, happiness and the menopause journey – I found a new passion in my fifties!

All that sounds great, but it wasn't plain sailing. Owing to my numerous symptoms and the negative impact they were having on my wellbeing, my GP started me on a high dose of oral synthetic HRT (chemically identical to women's hormones). I developed breakthrough bleeding and a burst ovarian cyst, which meant I ended up in hospital. I had an ultrasound scan, which showed thickening to the lining of my uterus, so was placed on a two-week waiting list for cancer biopsies and hysteroscopy.

The biopsies were negative, so I didn't need the hysteroscopy. Even though this was a worrying time, causing high levels of anxiety for those close to me, my main fear was that the gynaecologist would stop my HRT. Thankfully, he did not. Instead he suggested an alternative HRT, which was 'body identical' (the same molecular structure as a woman's hormones). This way, I could reduce my dose of HRT over a period of time, mimicking the body's natural decline in oestrogen in a controlled manner.

I tried a few different ways of taking oestrogen and progesterone, and I am now on a very small dose via a transdermal patch. I have made the choice to continue taking a low dose of transdermal HRT. I am aware that HRT has been in the news recently, linked to an increased risk of breast cancer. However, the breast-cancer risk from HRT is lower than some lifestyle risks, such as obesity and drinking alcohol. Instead, HRT offers me health benefits beyond symptom management by guarding me against the risk of osteoporosis and heart disease, both of which run in my family.

HRT is not for everyone. Some women can't take it or tolerate it and others wish to manage their symptoms naturally. This can be achieved by introducing lifestyle changes, including diet, exercise and reducing stress – it just takes a little bit longer to see the results. For me, taking HRT was an informed choice.

I feel healthier, happier, wiser and more confident than I ever have. I know exactly who I am and who I want to spend my time with, because I care less about what others think of me. Consequently, I'm thriving on a professional level by running a successful business helping other women transition smoothly through the menopause. I'm also flourishing on a personal level and enjoying a magnificent menopause. I did this by reframing the menopause as the beginning of a new and exciting era.

To me, it is about having freedom and newfound opportunities with a greater focus on myself. I believe I can still feel powerful and healthy far beyond the menopause years. That's not down to HRT alone but also hard work and many changes I've made to the way I live my life mentally, emotionally and physically. It has been worth it. It has been a liberating journey with highs and lows, but I have developed as a person in my own right. I am now back to being me – and so much more! I believe I am strong enough to cope with anything that life has to throw at me.

KELLY KAYSER

Kelly is an adventurer! She grew up in the West Country in the UK and after university she solo backpacked around the world. Never one to shy away from an adventure and fancying a change of lifestyle after 15 years of practicing law in London, she started a new life in a new country.

Kelly and her husband immigrated to Nova Scotia, Canada in March 2017. Whilst she continues to work in the legal environment, she is also embracing all things Canadian. Kelly lives on a lake and spends her time hiking, paddle boarding and sampling the local ciders. Living and loving life.

https://linkedin.com/in/kelly-kayser-641b5021/

https://instagram.com/kellyakayser/

Overcoming My Worst Fear

When I was at first school, three school friends died in a house fire; they were sisters. Their mum, dad and brother survived. Their home was destroyed by an electrical fire. Another school friend's dad was a fireman and lived a few yards down the road from their house; I remember hearing stories of how he tried to save them. It was heartbreaking and devastating. I also remember being so confused - how could this have ever happened? Since then – and perhaps even since before that – being in a fire is my worst fear. The unknown… How would you react if it happened to you? Could you escape? What could you do to prevent it? Always switch off plugs? My husband has always thought I was totally over the top always switching off appliances and switching off or pulling out plugs. It's just how I cope. Always trying to prevent something like that from happening to me.

Fast forward to May 8, 2018 at 2:30 am – as it turns out, you can't always prevent something like that from happening. I have run it over in my mind a million times and it had nothing to do with what I did or didn't do – the fire was deemed to be arson.

I woke up to hear a thudding sound – much like heavy rain. I always check the weather before bed for the next day and didn't remember any rain in the forecast. Curious, I looked out the bedroom window and, to my horror, all I could see was the glow of flames from around the corner of the building. Smoke was fiercely pouring out from underneath the guttering; the condo building I was living in on fire. I had to get out.

My beloved cat Charlie, who would normally hide under the bed at the slightest noise, was (thankfully) completely frozen on the bed knowing that something was wrong. I scooped him up, ran downstairs and put him in his carrier by the back door. I ran back upstairs and grabbed my phone, passport, rucksack, dressing gown and trainers. As I started to make my way back downstairs, smoke started to come through the ceiling in the hallway and the smoke alarms went off. I ran outside on to the back deck to call 911 and I distinctly recall how I couldn't remember my address – I just couldn't get the order of the numbers in the street address right. Thankfully they got the gist and said that the fire service should just be arriving – and they were.

I banged loudly on my immediate neighbours' door to try and wake them up in case they did not know. I could see that my other neighbour's apartment was fully on fire. I had to walk past their back door to get downstairs and once out into the parking lot, I could see the enormity of the fire. It was blazing three stories from the ground and up into the roof. I then realized I was basically trapped in the parking lot. I managed to get another neighbour to let me through their apartment and out onto the street.

There were crowds of people on the street watching, aghast. There were so many fire engines, so much smoke, but you couldn't appreciate the ferocity of the fire from the street. I stood watching with neighbours, praying that they put the fire out, praying my belongings and worldly possessions were saved. There were so many fire fighters working so hard to put it out. My husband had travelled to the UK for work the day before, so I had to let him know. He certainly didn't expect to receive a phone call from me so early in the day with that kind of news. He said I needed to let our friends know so that they could help me as he wouldn't be able to travel back to Canada until the next day. I waited until a more reasonable hour to let my friends know, but not to worry as Charlie and I were o.k. As soon as I had messaged them, they were straight on the phone to say they were on their way to pick us up. I had to explain that I was on a regular transit bus with the Red Cross some way up the street, wearing a purple 'dressing gown'. Various other friends then got in contact with me as the news of the fire broke across the city, all relieved to know we were all o.k.

I think I was then on autopilot – trying to process it and what I should be doing next. I would need to tell our landlord, my work, the insurance company, cancel my power, cable and generally sort things out. It took the fire department 12 hours to put out the fire and I spent a lot of time going back and forth to find out updates – I even saw myself on the local evening news as they reported the fire, still in my purple dressing gown. The fire department were nothing short of amazing – so empathetic and so much so, they could see my distress and were able to retrieve my laptop, wedding album and the folder containing all of our immigration paperwork. Just to have those few things meant so much and they worked just as tirelessly to help all of my neighbours. In the end, we had to wait several days to find out if we could ever get back into our apartment as there was a concern it was no longer structurally sound. I was so desperate to get back inside to see what had happened and also for my husband to see it. I didn't feel like I could get any sort of closure or get him to understand without seeing it.

We were allowed back in for a brief period, fully donned in hazmat suits. It was a horrific experience. It seems silly when I think back but I was convinced that my chest of drawers containing all of my underwear and gym clothes (I had extensive M&S and Sweaty Betty collections) would have survived as it was on the side of the apartment furthest from the fire. Imagine my absolute shock and horror to discover that the chest of drawers and its contents no longer existed. The fire had devastated our home. Walls were missing, insulation covered the floor, bits of roof were hanging down and I caught glimpses of sky and parts of things that used to be. The smell was noxious. We salvaged quite a few things – typically mainly my husband's clothes! We then began our own cleaning operation – trying to save on costs and ultimately, wanting to be the arbiter of what was salvageable or not, rather than someone at an insurance company. It was quite cathartic but also very hard for me. I realised just how much I had valued my possessions, especially my home comforts. I also realized how fortunate I had been to be able to have such things. I felt guilty for being ungrateful for being alive. Some people said, "Oh what fun! You can buy a whole new wardrobe!" In all honesty, it might sound like fun in theory but in practice, shopping under duress was no fun. I have to sincerely thank my mum who flew out to Canada the following month and endured numerous shopping trips with me.

The lesson in this for me is that bouncing back takes time and doesn't miraculously happen 'just like that'. I'm bouncing back from the fire and taking my time to do so. The effect events like these have on a person is very personal - people feel and experience things in different ways and as much as I don't like to admit it, I have had to accept that this has had a profound, deep affect on me. I certainly felt like there was an expectation that I was fine and could bounce back and move on with things, just like that. After all, there were no obvious physical injuries or scars on the outside.

Nothing has ever stopped me before or got in my way in that sense. I am pretty resilient and determined, fiercely independent and strong with a desire to succeed. So having to accept that that the fire had such a profound affect on me felt like failure: why can't I just forget about it, why do smoke alarms bother me, why do I worry, why do I still feel upset about all the things I lost, why would someone deliberately set fire to a building where people were peacefully sleeping? I can't visualise the person that did this, so I have to direct it somewhere and ultimately, I guess that means I bring it back on myself as there is nowhere else for it to go.

I really appreciate kindness and the value of friendship – bearing in mind we had only lived in Canada for just over a year when this happened and had no family close by. The kindness and generosity of our friends was unbelievable. Friends let us stay with them until we got back on our feet and found a new apartment. My book club brought me the most thoughtful care package I could have asked for and so many friends did so many kind things to help us out – I will be forever grateful.

If I could go back and give myself some advice, I would say: give yourself time, don't be hard on yourself and allow yourself to feel whatever it is you feel. For me, I think I was grieving. Grieving for the loss of our beautiful apartment, our home, loss of so many belongings. It may seem materialistic but I worked so hard to achieve certain things. They were my things, taken away from me unexpectedly. Don't get me wrong, I feel so utterly thankful that I reacted the way I did – calmly getting out with the actual essentials and didn't get hurt – but there has been a lot of guilt too: why didn't I grab this or that, or why didn't I go back in etc. It might seem completely ridiculous, but to me, I'd walked out in my pjs, no bra (!) and no clean clothes to change into, no make-up, no toothbrush, no shampoo. I also think that I attached a lot of comfort to my belongings from the UK. So, I had to start again from scratch. It was quite surreal. Imagine if one day you woke up and all your things had just gone!

So, do something for you to channel whatever it is you are feeling – in a positive way! I had already signed up to a 10 km race. I had never run that far in my life and decided I needed a challenge. I was in training and had new running shoes – they of course were lost in the fire along with literally all of my gym clothes. So after the fire, I pondered what to do, bought a new pair of running shoes and continued to ponder. I didn't do any training and then thought I would just give it a go anyway. It turns out that it very much was a case of mind over matter and I was able to channel all of my feelings into running that race. I did it in a respectable time and I ran it – all the way. This felt like an enormous achievement but I wasn't keen to repeat it. I then found myself signing up for another 10km in August 2019 and well, in 2020, who knows. It definitely won't be a marathon, but I will continue to find new ways to channel my feelings in a positive way.

KIRSTY VENGHAUS

Kirsty is a Coach, NLP Master & Rapid Transformational Therapist (RTT).

She is fascinated by the power of the human mind and how simple changes in how we think can have a huge impact on how successful and happy we are in business and life.

Kirsty helps clients create amazing personal transformations by helping them harness the power of their own minds so they can get off auto pilot and start living life to the full.

Kirsty believes everyone has the potential to make a difference in the world in their own way. But as we grow, we adopt belief systems that are limiting, so we never truly become who we can be.

Oh, and she also likes cats, sunshine and countryside!

www.transformwithkirsty.com

https://facebook.com/Transformwithkirsty

https://instagram.com/kirsty_venghaus/

https://linkedin.com/in/kirsty-venghaus/

Breaking Down To Breaking Through

If we're lucky, most of us have at least one defining moment in our life. A wake-up call that changes our perspective on how we should be living. Mine came in March 2013.

I was sitting in my car outside the Doctor's surgery. I had just been signed off work for 2 weeks due to 'stress and low mood'. According to the score on the Generalised Anxiety Disorder form I filled out I was depressed. My blood pressure was too high, I couldn't stop crying and I felt sick. I sat there for what seemed like an eternity, trying to comprehend what was happening to me. I wanted to go home but I couldn't remember how to drive the car.

That was the start of a very surreal, distressing, confusing and extremely isolating 9 months. My mind felt like it had broken and without it my body couldn't function properly either.

In the weeks that followed I had a shocking realisation:

"I think I've had a breakdown."

As I look back now it's so easy to see how I had got there. I had what I thought was a successful career in a financial services organisation. I was a project manager, regularly putting in 60 to 70 hour weeks. I was good at my job and used to working under sustained pressure, but the workload was relentless. Expectations were high (both mine and theirs). There was no time for eating properly, exercising, having a hobby, relaxing or generally doing anything except work.

Outside of work I was moving home and coping with the emotional and practical impact of my nan's ongoing battle with cancer. I was extremely close to her and when she passed away I didn't even have time to grieve. I just dealt with the practical side of paperwork, arrangements … anything except dealing with my emotions. To this day I don't even remember the funeral.

The 'obvious' signs that I wasn't well, such as anxiety, exhaustion, hyperactivity, sweats, heart palpitations and even hair loss went ignored. There were a few occasions where I almost passed out in the office. Worried friends staged an 'intervention' to get me to slow down. I just didn't see the problem. I'd been working under sustained stress for years and the feelings I had were so familiar they seemed normal.

Then the day came where my mind and body decided enough was enough. I was in the office, staring at the hundreds of emails pinging into my inbox, the phone kept beeping and ringing. When I didn't answer my colleagues would just come to find me. Suddenly time slowed down. Everything went out of focus and blurred. Sounds became muffled and distant. It was as if I was under water. Then I heard a voice in my head say, "I can't do this anymore." Cue sitting outside the Doctor's dazed and confused.

The first few weeks at home passed in a blur. The symptoms got worse, not better. I was so exhausted, walking across the room was like wading through concrete. Other times I had so much adrenaline rushing through my body I had to go out for several walks a day. I would often pace the house like a caged animal, crying and wringing my hands to get rid of pains in my hands and feet. My memory was so poor I'd forget what I was doing.

A trip to the supermarket caused a panic attack simply because I forgot what I'd gone in for. Lack of focus meant it became unsafe for me to drive. Extreme paranoia and anxiety pervaded my waking hours and at night I was tortured with my own spiralling negative thoughts. If I did eventually go to sleep, I'd often have nightmares resembling a disaster movie that were so real to me, I felt like I'd been running for hours.

Regular trips to the doctor saw me signed-off work for longer each time. Anti-depressants were offered and refused (a personal choice). Friends and family tried their best to help. If they contacted me to offer support, it was too much pressure. If they didn't, it meant no-one cared. I felt alone, misunderstood and helpless.

So here I was. Alone in my personal battle, just trying to get up every day and praying the cycle would stop.

The turning point came about 3 months in. I finally accepted that I was ill and that I wouldn't be able to go back to work, or even my life, until I got well.

My doctor was very understanding and empathetic, however at every visit I was encouraged to take anti-depressants and sleeping pills. They simply didn't have anything else to offer. I knew I wasn't depressed and at the time my mum had an addiction to prescription sleeping pills and painkillers which was destroying her physical and mental health. The thought of ending up in this situation terrified me; I needed to find another way.

I started to research stress and burnout. The more I studied, the more I realised how much I'd been neglecting my mental health. I came across the Human Givens approach and although I didn't think I had depression, I bought the book *How to Lift Depression Fast – the Human Givens Approach* by Joe Griffin & Ivan Tyrrell. This was an absolute gamechanger for me and the first time I'd ever given any thought to how my mind worked. From that, I knew exactly what had gone wrong for me. I was living life on auto-pilot in an emotional deficit. I had ignored all the signals from my body to slow down so it just rebelled and stopped.

I started Cognitive Behavioural Therapy which helped me unpick past trauma, deal with the grief for my nan, understand my work life was not normal or healthy and start to make a recovery plan. The saddest thing for me was realising I had no life outside of work.

Stability and routine were my first challenges. Getting a plan of doing vs relaxing was surprisingly hard! My habit of doing too much and trying to get everything right meant I would take 1 step forward and 2 steps back.

I continued to educate myself. I studied neuroscience, mindfulness and habits. I created a simple routine of exercise, healthy food and mindfulness. I journaled, practiced gratitude and meditated. Not very well I might add, but it was working.

It wasn't easy to re-build a life that had previously revolved solely around my career, however after trying out self-care routines, new hobbies and taking control of my thoughts I did it.

Fast forward a year and I was back into work with a whole new appreciation of what had gone wrong for me and what I needed to do to stay mentally and physically well. Although I wouldn't choose to go through that experience again, I wouldn't change it because without it, I would still be on auto-pilot.

So, what did I learn from it?

It can happen to anyone

Yes, even you. If you're 'lucky' enough to notice some of the symptoms, then do something about it now. Talk to someone, get some therapy, take some time out, adopt a self-care routine. Whatever you need.

Listen to your friends and family – if they're worried enough to share their concerns with you then there's probably something wrong even if you can't or won't see it. It's harder to climb out when you hit rock bottom.

People will not judge you for admitting you can't cope. When I returned to the office I felt like some secret world had opened up to me – at least half the people I spoke to (and that's conservative) had a similar personal experience and were relieved to share that with me. That's one of the reasons why I openly share my story; to encourage these conversations and help people understand the importance of looking after their mental health.

You can get off auto-pilot

Life is a rollercoaster of highs and lows. We can't control what happens to us, but we can control how we respond to it. The challenge is that the things that drive our thoughts, feelings and actions are outside of our conscious awareness.

Our mind needs to run as efficiently as possible, so nature gave us a nice energy saving auto-pilot solution: our subconscious mind. Everything goes in there. All of our beliefs, memories, everything we've ever experienced and made a meaning from and every action we ever took, is recorded and stored. So, when an external event happens, your mind goes through the records, finds a best match for that situation and runs a program. The thing is, it may not be the most appropriate program anymore but it's so fast and automatic we don't catch it running!

So get self-aware. Start journaling, notice your thought patterns and what triggers you. Get therapy to fix what you can't address on your own.

There is hope

I needed to believe this more than anything when I was ill. I searched endlessly for reassurance that I would get better and I wanted a timescale for when that would happen. Even when I did recover enough to go back to work, I spent months worrying that it might happen again. I just wanted to be 'normal'.

So as someone who has gone from breaking down to breaking through - I'm here to tell you this:

There is hope. You can get better. You can feel 'normal' again.

Burnout isn't just caused by overwork and stress. Simply feeling unhappy day to day and not living your true purpose can do it too. It usually takes a crisis for us to take stock of our lives and do the inner work needed to create a healthy mind and re-connect with our true selves. Don't wait until you hit crisis, you can make small steps now towards a more fulfilling life.

After my experience I realised I wasn't living my purpose, so I retrained as an NLP Master, Life Coach and Clinical Hypnotherapist. I now have my own business and love helping people to heal and create the life they dream of.

One certainty in life is that there will be change you didn't choose; challenges you'd rather not face; choices you didn't want to make. But if you have strong mental foundations, you'll build the resilience and skills to get through – maybe slightly battered, but not broken.

LOUISE JONES

I'm a determined lady in her 50s, happily married with a lovely family and wide group of friends. I always wanted a job role supporting other people; I worked hard, went to university then worked in local government in public health. I worked in two Councils over 30 years, working passionately, but then I crashed. I almost lost everything and had to build a new "me". I built myself back up through creativity, recovery courses and volunteering.

I am now working for the National Health Service, I still throw myself into volunteering and enjoy family time with my dog and stand up paddle-boarding.

Crafting A New Life

I don't feel like I can share my journey to recovery with anyone without putting it in context; how I got myself into such a dark place, what caused the mental health crisis and also how bad it got for me.

I worked hard all my life. Always determined and passionate about everything I got involved with. I worked in public health for over 30 years and the organisation I worked for went through a ruthless, tough, drawn-out cost saving reorganisation, all as a result of Conservative austerity measures. Whatever your political view, how I was treated was cruel. Competing with colleagues for roles in a harmful, damaging, unfair manner, knowing any one of us could lose our jobs and everything that went with it. I believe I was misled, lied to and, although I kept a role in the new organisation, I ended up completely burnt out. It was far more complicated than that, but that is the essence of what happened. I recall staring one day at the office photocopier not having a clue how to work it. On another day when hot desking, I sat at my desk with tears running down my face, staring at the screen; my mind was full of fog, no-one around me cared, new staff were in and didn't know me so I became invisible and unable to speak.

I was signed off with workplace stress. The shame of it! I used to judge people that used to go off with stress! Once off work my mental health declined rapidly. I honestly thought there would be good mental health services that would scoop me up and fix me. Unfortunately, these already 'Cinderella' (neglected) services were also hit hard with austerity and so I was on long waiting list after long waiting list, but once I got to meet someone for support I was shocked with the level and quality of service on offer.

Days went into weeks; weeks went into months. I was switching and changing antidepressants on the advice of my GP like a child being offered choices in a pick and mix sweet shop. I got to the point that I no longer wanted to feel this low anymore and felt like I had no hope for my future. I felt like a huge, heavy weight of a burden on my family and friends. Everyone would be better off without me. Some years previously I had lost five stone in a year, now I'd put six stone back on through self-isolation, self-loathing, underactivity, medication and comfort eating. I was in a bad place and desperately wanted out of this cycle.

I recall one low point - I'm in the sea walking backwards. There's a police helicopter above me, a lifeboat behind me, but it can't come close to me due to the rocks in the sea. In front are my personal Angels, my heroes; two scared, concerned policemen. They have already been trying to calm my hysteria for a while, with little success. It's September, the tide is coming in and the sea state is rough. They have already tried to throw a lifesaving line to me, but I don't care and don't want to be rescued. I'm in self-destruct determined mode. I'm getting pounded by the waves hitting me from behind. The heroes are wading in too, we're all going in deeper and deeper. I'm going in backwards so can't see what's coming, but I see their faces; I'm out of my depth now. Then something changes. A huge wave slams into my back and this strange sound is pulled out of my body like air being squeezed out of a bagpipe. It's a guttural sound, so clear that the policemen hear it too despite all the noise from the sea and the helicopter above; none of us forget this sound. I don't feel anything, my body is still numb and my adrenaline is pumping fast now.

From this moment everything changes within me and I want to be rescued; I want to live. The policeman throws the line again for the 3rd time, if I don't reach it now I'm lost to the sea forever. But I can't see the line or the orange buoy it's attached to. I'm desperately trying to see it, the policeman calls out, "Try to feel it with your hands!" My hands are searching furiously under the waves for the rope, I feel completely blind and it seems hopeless, then my fingers feel it and I cling onto it for dear life. This is my umbilical cord and it is my lifeline now; I can't let go of it. I am pulled in, I am rescued. Unfortunately, my mental health is still in a deep pit and I continue for months on a roller coaster of attempts - always going to the same secluded beach, to the sea. I fill myself with such self-hatred and disgust with myself after any attempt, knowing the waste of resources I have caused and the pain I have caused my husband, family and friends who all feel helpless.

Fast forward time and we've moved on 3 years. I'm working for the National Health Service in the community, supporting vulnerable clients. I love my life; I still have ups and downs but I'm far more resilient. I love my family and friends and I'm grateful they all stood by my side throughout. I know I'm a different person, that first version has long gone, but this one has many qualities that I like. She knows how to support people in crisis that's for sure and she can positively influence people's downward spirals in a way that many professionals can't. How did I get to this point? What changed the destructive path?

It took a long time to work this out, but after trying so hard searching for the right kind of recovery I discovered that I had to find my own recovery jigsaw pieces. I tried various medications, cognitive behavioural therapy, acupuncture, counselling, but none of these helped me enough. Some even made my condition worse. I threw myself into crafting, mainly painting to begin with; I painted how I was feeling and events that took place. The crisis in the sea was painted in acrylic with a similar feel to Edvard Munch's, "The Scream." I recall a support worker asking me what my outlet for stress was, "Was it drugs, alcohol, what?" She asked and I replied, "I just can't stop crafting." I was mortified when she turned to her student and said, "I've never heard of that drug before."

I knew I had to do this myself; to find out the slow, hard way what worked for me and what didn't. I needed to find my own jigsaw pieces and each piece would represent something I would try to help my mental health. If it worked I would keep the piece, if it didn't it would be like shoving a piece that was the wrong shape into your puzzle. No matter how hard you try to make it fit, if it's not right for you stop trying as it will break and you won't be able to complete the puzzle or your recovery. A completed puzzle doesn't mean everything is perfect, but it's certainly a better picture than before. As life changes and we change so do the puzzle pieces.

My recovery jigsaw puzzle pieces included getting a rescue dog; she helped me to get out of the house and speak to people again. I had also developed a terrible stutter, partly due to never sleeping properly. I was lucky that my GP got me a quick referral to a speech therapist and she was the most incredibly supportive woman who really understood mental health, she showed genuine compassion and care. The medication I was on was a constant conversation with my GP and took a long time to get right, but now I'm off everything which in itself was very hard. This is not right for everyone and always speak to your GP about changes to medication. I attended various recovery courses and enjoyed meeting others with similar feelings to mine; at long last I didn't feel so isolated and had people to talk to without fear of judgement or repercussion.

When you work you have many connections with other people. You have a role where you may feel valued. My old work gave me so much, including a great sense of satisfaction supporting people and making a difference. I had a sense of purpose and structure, I felt respected and people would listen to me. When you're at home all the time, your mind is your worst enemy; filled with wanting to destroy the person you used to be and with self-hatred. I distanced myself from everyone and life changed very rapidly.

I had an amazing group of friends who tried so hard to support me. I kept painting and crafting, making things and giving so many creative items away which did make me feel good. Things slowly started to move in the right direction. Then I decided I wanted to do something more and have structure in my week. I thought I could volunteer, that way if it got too much I could bail out at any time. I found a local charity that wanted support on the craft table, they supported vulnerable women. That was the biggest turning point.

The interview went well, but it was touch and go as to whether I would end up attending as a vulnerable woman needing support or a creative volunteer. Thankfully I passed and held it together to get the role. I was flying so high from this point onwards, all of a sudden the attention was not on me but on others. I listened, I cared and I supported them with creative empowering tools, which fed into my recovery. I also started running courses for the recovery group that had helped me and again this was very empowering. I loved every bit of it all. I knew I was really making a difference to people's lives. I often used the five ways to wellbeing: Connect/Learn/Active/Notice/Give in creative tools to encourage recovery in others.

Then the time felt right to take a step back into the world of work. I had my first interview and I got the job. It's not been easy, I continue to struggle at times, but I'm incredibly resilient these days. I continue to be passionate about supporting others as I know how low you can feel and that's a horrible dark pit to be in. So, consider your recovery as a jigsaw puzzle and good luck finding all the right pieces to support you through the tough times, remembering those pieces will change too over time.

LOUISE MCMILAN

Louise is in her late 40s and lives in the seaside town of Weston-Super-Mare.

Following a HR career of over 20 years, Louise is now an Inspirational Speaker on her personal experience of Mental Health and Breast Cancer. She also works 1 to 1 with women, helping them overcome their limiting self-belief and lack of self-confidence. Louise's passion is to empower others to 'live life more fully' on their terms.

In addition, Louise and her friend Teresa Ridley, have co-founded a Breast Cancer Group in Weston called Weston Cancer Support Group. They meet on the first Monday of the month at Weston Hospice

hello@louisemcmilan.co.uk

www.louisemcmilan.co.uk

https://linkedin.com/in/louisemcmilan

https://facebook.com/louisemcmilancoaching

https://instagram.com/living_life_more_fully/

Cancer Was The Making Of Me!

Do you ever feel like you are living your life as different people? I began to realise I was and I really struggled to understand who I truly am.

There was the me who I portrayed at work, the version of me that my family and friends see and the one I feel I really am – but am not confident enough to be.

I've suffered from limiting self-belief and lack of self-confidence for most of my life. Growing up felt like constant put downs, non-constructive criticism and nit picking. This came from a number of places – family, school and college friends, teachers, work colleagues and managers. Looking back, even mere acquaintances seemed to have a negative view and impact.

As an adult this turned into anxiety and unfortunately, on a few occasions, depression. I would constantly:

- Compare myself to others

- Question if I was good enough at anything - not even the simplest task, let alone to reach any dreams or aspirations

- Over analyse every situation or conversation so I could find the negative, then multiply it by 100 and replay it constantly

- Believe everyone else had a better life, better figure, prettier, nicer, happier and what I saw they had would never happen to me

And this was before social media!

From my perspective, with my limiting beliefs, I had a successful career in HR for over 20 years. I even got my professional qualifications. However, because I didn't believe in myself it exacerbated my anxiety, my overthinking, procrastination and my conviction that I was going to stuff it up – and I admit on occasions, I did!

The problem with my limiting self-belief and lack of confidence is that it didn't just affect my work; it affected my friendships and relationships, especially as I got older.

As I got into my mid to late 30s I started to get anxious about socialising. If we were going out for the evening I would get myself into such an anxious state that I'd end up cancelling 2 nights before just so I could calm myself down. If we were just meeting for a cuppa I'd change about 6 times. I felt I never had the right clothes, I felt I never had anything interesting to say – I questioned why people would want to spend time with me.

To compensate for all of this, I put pressure on myself to do my best at what I could, and I mean a *lot* of pressure. I would work long hours, over prepare, over think, double check and seek approval. All it did was cause me burnout and to not eat properly. I became paranoid and constantly thought the worst. The impact was that I was on edge, tearful and sluggish. I had constant mouth ulcers, never just one. I would get up, go to work, come home and go straight to bed. This would carry on for days, if not weeks.

My last major episode happened in October 2016 and resulted in medication again just before Christmas 2016. I remember that Christmas feeling very numb and not enjoying a moment of it. I decided that 2017 was all about rebuilding myself again; I didn't know how or what, but knew I had to find the strength and courage to make some major changes to how I was living.

Then I had the biggest 'plot twist' of my life! I was diagnosed with breast cancer.

Now, I will tell you how my cancer was diagnosed as I didn't find a lump and I wasn't having a routine mammogram. In April 2017 I noticed a discharge from my left breast on the bedclothes I wore to bed. It happened a few times over a couple of weeks so I booked in to see my GP. Both breasts were examined and nothing seemed untoward, however I was going to be referred to the hospital 'to be on the safe side'. I had an appointment to see a consultant who examined me and, again, he couldn't see or feel anything untoward and thought it was probably a blocked milk duct, but would refer me for some tests 'to be on the safe side'.

My mammogram came through quite quickly and then I was invited in for an ultrasound. They did the ultrasound on both breasts and I was told they needed to do a biopsy from my right breast. As you can imagine I queried this as it was my left I had a concern with. They did the ultrasound all over again on both and confirmed there was something there on my right. I have to admit to still not really thinking much of it and neither did my mum. I had not long started a new job and was trying not to let the cretin rule my head and use my tools to manage my anxiety.

Monday 12th June is the day it all changed and is now affectionally referred to as my Cancerversary. I was told they detected cancer in my right breast. They believed my cancer was stage 2 and 25mm. As you can imagine, we were stunned. On my way back to the car all I could think of was naming my tumour, I called it Stan. My Lumpectomy happened the following week and I had to wait 2 weeks for the results.

The results were that my tumour was larger; it was 45 mm, not 25mm and stage 3, not stage 2. They removed 3 lymph nodes and 2 were positive for cancer which meant I was going to have to receive Chemotherapy.

Now … let's just say my body decided that this was all too easy. A week after my first chemo I started to get stomach ache; some days were worse than others. To cut a long story short, the week of my 2nd chemo I was diagnosed with Appendicitis.

I'll never forget the consultant's words when he came back with my test results. He said, "You are a very, very poorly young lady. You are not at all well." It had turned into an abscess, which was now stuck to my bowel and colon, so I had to undergo major emergency surgery. I was in intensive care for 2 days, had a blood transfusion, along with my hair falling out. I came out of ITU the night before my 45th birthday. Due to this surgery I was in hospital for 2 weeks and my Chemo was delayed for 7 weeks.

After my Chemo finished at Christmas I had to continue with my Herceptin injections (18 in total) and 4 weeks of radiotherapy in Bristol. At the Bristol Royal Infirmary you get to ring a bell when your Radiotherapy treatment finishes. I was so relieved this was the end I rang the bell and broke it! The handle came off in my hand – only I could do that.

How did this change me?

During my treatment I did something that not only surprised my family and friends, but also me! I decided that I was going to be bald. I wasn't going to wear the scarves I bought or even my wig! I'd walk down the high street; I'd walk along the sea front; go out for coffee or meals - bald! This was me being determined to manage my cancer journey my way and I gave myself permission to do so.

I learned that I do have a lot of friends. People do like me and I remember being overwhelmed by the amount of support I had; the cards, the messages, the flowers, the offers of meeting for coffee. The support was tremendous and absolutely overwhelming.

My major learning though is that mindset plays a powerful part in how you deal with situations, your wellbeing and how you live your life. For me, by being strong, positive, believing in myself and that I was going to beat cancer and do things my way made me realise that I can accomplish anything that I put my mind to. I found myself being more relaxed about situations and just focusing on what I was going to do that day.

One of the main things is that I've stopped living a life of what I believe others expect of me and I do what makes me happy. It's been a wakeup call to remind me that life is too short. I knew I had to make some changes to my life and ok, I admit I have wasted some of my life, but there was and is nothing I could do to change that.

My cancer journey gave me new strength and belief in myself. Strength and belief I didn't know I had. I remember my mum saying that I was handling this journey better than she thought I would or better than she would and so did some friends. Until you are in this position you don't know how you will react.

In a very bizarre way, I think cancer was the making of me! There are times when I wish I was back in my cancer bubble, because it was the only thing I had to concentrate on. But if I can get through all that has happened to me, with a smile on my face and my lippy on, I can face any challenge head on.

So, where am I now? My passion now is to help other people overcome their limiting self-belief, lack of self-confidence and anxiety and to help them to achieve their dreams and live life as they wish. I'm a believer that we all have the answers within us and the ability to make changes, we just need support to find them, believe in them and make things happen.

The forming of the cancer group

In the spring of 2019, I met Teresa Ridley at Weston Business Women's networking group. I mentioned that I had breast cancer and she invited me for coffee. After sharing our stories, we talked about different support available and what was needed in Weston. It was there that Weston Breast Cancer Group was born.

The group has now grown, with women from outside of Weston such as Bristol and Bridgwater. We have also been joined by women who have experienced other cancers, so as a group we changed our name to Weston Cancer Group. The aim of the group is to provide a safe and confidential space for women to share their story, provide a bit of laughter, companionship and support. We want everyone to feel good about themselves again.

MAISIE TIPPLE

My name is Maisie, I'm 20 years old and I'm delighted to enclose my personal bounce back story with you. I'm an aspiring writer who transforms my thoughts into art. I wish to uplift others with my words, contributing to a stronger society which values every individual's narrative. I'm a left-wing activist, protesting for the minority groups who are unheard and spreading as much love as possible on the internet. I practice spirituality regularly, as it's precious to me and my identity. I'm a proud representative of the LGBTQ+ community, cat lover, plant mummy, vegetarian and pacifist.

maisiempower.wordpress.com

https://instagram.com/maisietipplex/

https://instagram.com/maisiepoetry/

The Rising Phoenix

Warning: This chapter contains references to Sexual Abuse

In this chapter, I will concentrate on Borderline Personality Disorder (BPD) and my sexual abuse story. I'll delve into some struggles I faced, how I overcame and still overcome such adversity.

BPD is otherwise recognised as an emotionally unstable personality: it's diagnosed using nine criteria from the diagnostic and statistical manual of mental disorders. To qualify for a diagnosis, you must identify with five or higher of the following traits: fear of abandonment, self-mutilation, suicidal ideation, dissociation, uncontrollable anger, mood swings, distorted sense of self, unstable relationships and self-destructive behaviour.

At 15 I was referred to the child mental health services where they identified my condition as anxiety and depression. Many professionals believe it's impossible to diagnose BPD during adolescence and they provide an under-diagnosis, which was my experience. This occurrence prohibited my recovery; I could not receive speciality care and they mis-treated my illness.

Thereafter, I enrolled in counselling to no avail; it was demoralising to be so misunderstood. They offered me inadequate guidance, like taking baths or going for walks to combat suicidal thoughts and self-harming urges. When I declared the inadequacy of these techniques, my counsellor offered no substitutes. As a result, I started refusing further treatments and the newfound hopelessness overwhelmed me. I took anti-depressants as a solution, but in actuality they worsened my condition. I persuaded myself that they weren't potent enough, so I increased the dosage whenever I felt unfit.

I was drifting like an invisible cloud; impulsive, careless and self- absorbed. I sought to preserve consistent relationships yet sabotaged my friendships. This would result in explosive arguments because of my denial, rage and unpredictability. I considered the fluctuation their fault, and I was the victim. My companions became interchangeable and my views on individuals ranged from absolute adoration to hatred. I looked at the world through a delusional black and white telescope which filtered out most sensibility.

Throughout my teenage years, I dated suspicious men in their 20s. They had groomed me online and I accepted their manipulation in my vulnerable state. I was heartbroken over the first break-up with a partner. I attended plenty of house parties where I used alcohol to numb the grief of his absence and even when the pain dwindled, my substance abuse issue did not.

I became reliant on booze to lessen my issues and, as I was underage, it usually took drastic measures to get some.

The night my previous partner had gotten back from his vacation after he'd missed my prom, my mum and I argued. I was supposed to meet him and my mum disallowed these plans as an adequate punishment. I felt devastated and crammed all the alcohol I could find in the kitchen into my handbag to go and drown all of my sorrows.

Once I had swallowed it all, I approached an older male who I'd communicated with before on Tinder and who was still prowling on my Facebook profile. I urged him to meet up with me and purchase cider. After I'd persuaded him, I crept out. This moment brought forth tragic consequences and additional trauma I would devote months upon months seeking to abolish. This was the date I had non-consensual sex.

It's the tragedy you tell yourself doesn't occur to people you know, let alone yourself. I felt unsafe leaving my home and I welcomed my life as an agoraphobic. I forced myself to take a bus trip and it was the most depressing task; I sobbed all the way on the route there and the trek home. Not long after, I took part in the National Citizen Service, which raised my confidence and pushed me to return to some form of youthful normality.

I enlisted in therapy again at an unbelievable organisation which specialises in sexual abuse cases and they really helped me. I studied how to use tapping to handle my triggers and stresses. I've looked my attacker in the eyes, I've fought my fears and I'm no longer hanging on by a flimsy thread, which is so simply snapped.

The biggest lesson of this whole situation is you can defeat events which are labelled as undefeatable. The things society choose to ignore are valid to address and grow from because they're all part of the nature of humanity. It can be cruel and beauteous.

I'm surviving despite this major upheaval and it's turned into something I need not tend to because I've forgiven and I'm content now. I never let it wreck my life, I let it calm down until it had limited influence over me.

When I arrived at the age of 18, I was ostracised by my best friends. I'd announce my everyday thoughts like before and I'd get harsh judgment in return. Petty behaviour was demonstrated by one of my dearest girlfriends with degrading comments left on my social media accounts. One night, I got home from work and logged onto Snapchat, observing my friends nightclubbing without me the day before. This suffering was unbearable and I published a rushed suicide note expressing my goodbyes. I continued to overdose on tablets I'd discovered in the medication cabinet.

Before I knew it, this friend had entered my household and requested an ambulance whilst other associates comforted my hysterical nan. The paramedics connected me to a drip and I became extremely ill; vomiting and hearing voices. I made a quick recovery and was discharged once my mental health had been assessed.

My mother kept me on suicide watch to ensure no further harm was caused, she locked away all potentially harmful objects and I wasn't granted much time outside.

After returning to my nan's, devastation struck. I had bolted myself in the lavatory, producing a detailed suicide note consisting of everything from personalised letters to funeral arrangements. Phone calls were made and the law enforcement and paramedics appeared.

This second attempt was the most revolutionary. It was this incident which prompted my psychoanalysis with a psychiatrist. I had regained faith; I had something to cling onto. I joined Facebook groups and I cherished becoming involved in a supportive community.

My counsellor was trained in both CBT and DBT, in my opinion the finest methods of emotional regulation.

During recovery, I came back to my mother's home. It was in this period that direct messages were delivered via Instagram summarising all the catastrophic effects of my negative actions towards this girlfriend. She made legitimate criticisms, generating more room for me to advance by recognising these faults with my counsellor, so we could work to resolve them.

Mental illness is an ongoing battle; I still undergo periods of regression. It takes continual effort and positive reinforcement. It's acknowledging what stability means and what you must sacrifice to get there. You may have to give up toxic relationships, unfulfilling careers and other things which don't promote your happiness. It's isolating and hurtful. However, you'll learn to surround yourself with attentive and pure-hearted individuals. You'll tackle your goals and ambitions to achieve more.

Occasionally, it's challenging to leave my bed and progress with the day. Yet, I rise and adhere to routine; I assure you it helps and I guarantee it gets better. I retreat in nature, meditate, journal, consume enough water, avoid sugary foods, eat a balanced diet and record my emotions daily. I'm drinking more non-alcoholic alternatives because alcohol is a depressant which disturbs my ability to behave appropriately.

I'm not advising that anybody does the same as I do. I know illnesses of any kind are nuanced and healing takes different actions from person to person. My best advice would be to keep fighting, whatever that requires you to do.

I kept battling for a diagnosis and the correct support. It wasn't simple; I submerged myself in anguish for years and overlooked my selfishness with a victim mindset. It caused those who care for me such agony and concern, but the guilt will consume you enough to send you on a spiral; acceptance is the key to motivating yourself forward.

You can change your future with the proper amount of effort and courage. Determination lies within all humans; it's always accessible and can be used to manage deteriorating mental or physical health. It is endurance which creates the most successful outcomes and individuals. It is endurance which generates the most rewarding results, empowered lives and inspiring stories.

My world has slowly recovered because of my perseverance. I'm surrounded by a small circle of beautiful friends. My self-confidence and respect are paramount to me, so I won't jeopardise either. I'm learning to embrace my authentic individuality and my potential on an eternal journey of self-improvement.

NICKY COLLINS

I'm Nicky, The Autism Coach. Did you know that the majority of autism research has been carried out on males, which means females who display autism differently to our male counterparts often go misdiagnosed or undiagnosed? I know this as I was one of those women. It took me 34 years to realise I'm on the spectrum, that a lifetime of anxiety and depression was closely linked to a neurological difference. With the knowledge I gained from my own experiences I now offer workshops, individual therapy and coaching to those who are open to learning about the behaviour behind autism and ways in which autism can be a superpower rather than a hindrance.

www.theautismcoach.co.uk

https://linkedin.com/in/nicky-collins-9b1b89141/

https://facebook.com/MysticalForestCoaching

Unmasked

Established in 1984, I came into this world as a blank canvas; ignorant, naked and scared. And, just like you, a series of events and experiences shaped the person I am today.

Anxiety and depression have been a part of my life for as long as I can remember. If it wasn't me, it was someone close to me struggling to keep their head above water. My own struggles became apparent when I was 13 years old. I was planning on running away from home with a boy from school. He got cold feet and in my depressed mind the only viable option I had was to end my life. All I really remember from that time is being so violently ill that I was vomiting through my nose as well as my mouth. Oh, and the kindness my grandad showed me that day. He stroked my hair and was kind with his words; my mother was concerned but highly stressed. He counteracted her worry and made me feel calm, which goes to show how the little things can make such a big difference. My grandad was a kind man, grumpy at times, but I would stand and brush what little hair he had for ages and he was the only person who could brush mine without hurting me. His death when I was 16 was my first experience of loss; I had nightmares for years after.

The year I turned 16 was a big year; it was the year I gained independence. I certainly wasn't mature, or ready for it, but there was no choice. My mother had reached the end of her parenting capacity and wanted me gone. Helping me to move from the family home into a hostel for young people, she paid the deposit for my key and first weeks' rent and then it was all down to me. I was in my final year of school, drawing benefits to provide for myself financially. I was cooking my own meals, doing my own washing, being responsible for my time management and the company I kept. I had all the chores of a responsible adult and then they wanted me to sit in stuffy classrooms with teachers who had little to no respect for me; who treated me like a child. My classmates alienated me as I wasn't like them. I never had been but now the differences were even more obvious to see. Life was challenging and it wasn't a huge surprise when I went off the rails.

My rebellion had long since kicked in and I point blank refused to go to school. Instead I went to the pub and drank heavily. I also started to dabble in drugs. One day I was handed crack cocaine; my life was turning into a substance fuelled haze. Fortunately I woke up one day and never touched the hard stuff again. I am convinced my grandad in his spirit form intervened and helped me back onto the right path. Whatever the cause, crack was out of my life. Alcohol, however, remained my crutch and twisted best friend for many more years.

It was during my 16th year that I fell into a relationship with a man 17 years my senior. He had a well-paid job and filled the parental void I had found myself facing. We got married, had a child and then I realised that my heterosexual phase was over and we divorced. Divorce wasn't so scary for me, my parents had married and divorced each other 3 times by the time I reached my early 20's... Is that a record?!

Fast forward to 2010 and life was the best it had ever been. I married my now ex-wife and started a wellness business through a well-known network marketing company, helping people to achieve their weight goals. In that time I spent many hours working on my own personal development journey and it was that work that was to later save my life.

2011 was the start of a slippery slope into a very dark place. I lost my nan in the October, my marriage collapsed in the November and I moved 80 miles away for a fresh start in February 2012, which was shortly after my mother decided she didn't want contact with me anymore. I simply didn't meet her expectations and having been told for years that I wouldn't amount to anything because we weren't 'that type' of family, it's hardly surprising that I was a little off track.

Roll on to May 2012 and my whole world collapsed. It was Saturday the 12th and it happened to be one of those rare days where summer makes an early appearance; the sun was shining and there wasn't a cloud in the sky. My mood was great until it suddenly plummeted for no apparent reason. I took myself off so as not to affect anybody else and when I was asked if I was OK I said no, but I couldn't pinpoint what the problem was. We decided to head home and relax, but I didn't get a chance to take off my shoes before the door went. Looking out of the window I saw two police officers on the doorstep; it was the British Transport Police and they were here to tell me about my dad's death. After confirming who I was, they told me that he had laid on the train tracks the night before; that he had been hit and killed by a train. My dad and I had our ups and downs over the years, but I was always a daddy's girl; it was his lap I would clamber into when I was poorly, it was him who I looked up to and adored and now he was gone.

As you can imagine my own mental health took a nosedive. I wasn't living, I was existing. My goals were to get up each day and get my son to school, sliding into the 'blissful' unawareness that alcohol provided at the end of each day. Between 2012 and 2015 my life was a blur. My grief closed me down, making me appear selfish and self-centred when in reality I needed time and support to heal. I then slid into the worst possible type of relationship with an unmedicated schizophrenic narcissist. I relocated over 100 miles away to her hometown and shortly after found myself and my son homeless. Looking back, this was me running from my problems; always relying on outside sources to fuel my happiness. Inadvertently, this self-destructive character taught me how to use my empathy to the max. She taught me some of the ways my anxiety and depression were triggered and she taught me what wasn't OK.

I realised I didn't want to put anyone through what I had experienced and was still experiencing. I knew that whatever battles I faced I would come out stronger than before. At the time I felt so angry - that deep raw anger where all you want to do is scream, whilst feeling empty and numb. Where everything you see annoys you - which fitted so well with the lack of empathy I had developed through dad's death. I swore to myself that his death wouldn't be in vain. I redirected my anger so I could help others; promising myself I would break out of the victim mindset and use those experiences to develop myself and others.

I was a shell. I was going through the mechanics of living. I cared little about others and nobody truly wants to be that person. When I did make an effort, when I put on that smile and tried to socialise, every part of me was screaming to go home, back to safety.

I had reached my absolute bottom; the only way from there for me was up or out. I tried to get out and although I was close, I failed and turned my life around one day at a time.

My personal development work finally came back to light during the later stages of 2015. I'd had enough; I wanted to live. I didn't want to be this shell of a person any more, I wanted to thrive and live life to my full potential. I stepped away from the victim persona that I had created for myself. I started to use the tools I'd collected from my personal development. I started to train in other areas and use my own experiences to help people. There isn't a single therapy I offer within my practice that I haven't used myself; I've had powerful and life changing experiences with all of them, experiences that would be a chapter in themselves!

I learned that most of my anxiety, especially my social anxiety, came from undiagnosed autism. This realisation gave me a whole new opportunity to evolve into a much more authentic and aligned version of myself and opened me up to helping other women. Women like me, who had slipped through the medical net and had been labelled as depressed when actually we are just super sensitive to our surroundings and have spent a lifetime blending in to try and fit into what society considers normal. I am far from normal and so are my autistic brothers and sisters; we are wired differently. We are unique and that uniqueness is something to celebrate, not something to put in a box and hide away.

Through the loss of my dad I started to learn exactly who I was. I didn't understand how life could be so cruel when he took his life, yet in time his death led me on a journey that has inspired me, strengthened me and connected me to my spiritual side. It has shown me who I am in mind, body and spirit. His last act could be seen as selfish, but really, it was the greatest gift of all.

NICKY MARSHALL

Nicky is an award winning, international speaker and best-selling author, seasoned workplace facilitator and mentor. She is also a mum, nan and wife and loves nothing more than family time.

At 40, Nicky suffered and recovered from a disabling stroke - inspiring a life's mission to make a bigger difference.

Nicky has an accountancy background and 20 years of helping people improve their health and wellbeing under her belt. Combining both, Nicky inspires people to discover their own brand of Bounce!

With passion in buckets and a penchant for keeping it simple, Nicky has a unique talent in breaking down the barriers that hold people back from living a life they love. Be careful if you stand too close - her enthusiasm rubs off!

www.discoveryourbounce.com

https://facebook.com/discoveryourbounce

https://twitter.com/_nickymarshall

https://linkedin.com/in/nickymarshall

https://youtube.com/channel/UCBXK2Ut7IyL39-Pc1cRr2lA

Sanity Not Vanity

Having babies is natural right? It's what we, as women, were designed to do.

I had always wanted children. Growing up in a loving household I had always just assumed I would meet someone, get married and have children. I had never considered anything else and so, as my dream unfolded, I couldn't wait to start a family and meet my future babies.

I was very lucky that the conceiving part was easy. Knowing so many that struggle, that had never been a worry of mine. Apart from a bit of morning sickness, I loved being pregnant and both of my beautiful girls arrived within 5 hours of labour.

However, after having Kassi, my second daughter, I had two major life challenges to deal with; my then husband's actions surrounding her birth destroyed our marriage (though it took another 8 years to actually happen) and my granddad, a massive part of my life, died suddenly.

It seemed as if my body buckled under the weight of carrying my emotions. I started having 3 week, really heavy periods and was in constant daily pain. My mornings would start by crawling to get the girls ready to take Ami to nursery, as standing was just too much for me.

My stomach bloated so much that I was always being asked when my third was due, so I started wearing shapeless, long and flowing clothes to hide my swollen, painful belly. On bad days I would look around seven months pregnant and the thought of going anywhere would make me anxious. My periods were so heavy and unpredictable; I would sometimes call my mum from the bath to ask her to do the school run, as I was afraid to go anywhere.

I remember once being at a friend's house, sitting on a pale lemon Laura Ashley chair. I stood to take my cup to the sink and as I did I felt a gush. By the time I had wildly made my excuses, left and drove home the car seat was covered in blood – good job the girls were in school at this point, they would have been terrified!

For three years my severe prolapse went undiagnosed despite countless visits to GPs and a consultant and although my time with my girls was still lovely, I felt only half a mum. My marriage was miserable due to events surrounding Kassi's birth and I had pretty much resigned myself to this life.

Thanks to the concern of my mum and a wonderful locum doctor, life changed. The prolapse was picked up and within weeks I had a hysterectomy. My recovery was swift and post op I was amazed at how I looked: the pain in my face had gone.

Over the next few years so much changed. I got better, I got fitter, I completed my accountancy exams and got the job I had been working for. My marriage came to an end during this time, badly, but the girls and I set ourselves on a new track and I had the health, energy and headspace to be the mum I wanted to be.

Two years later, after several boyfriends and a LOT of lessons, I met Phil.

Phil was a lovely, regular guy who didn't carry the emotional baggage that other dates had. He was funny, sexy and looked at me in a way that no one else ever had. He wanted to know what I liked, what I wanted – both in and out of the bedroom. This was new and exciting - and terrifying!

My confidence had been properly bashed out of me in a controlling marriage and my body image was through the floor. While the bloating had now gone, along with the three-week periods, my tummy was a baggy, saggy mess covered in stretch marks. When I looked in the mirror I avoided that bit… well, avoided mirrors that were longer than shoulder length if I could. I still wore the floaty tops, something that Phil commented on as he thought I had a lovely figure.

Any time we were close, if his hand touched my stomach I would freeze. It was as if my entire physical and emotional trauma was locked in the ball of my abdomen and I wanted to hide it all. I had healed my life, stood up to abuse and moved forward in leaps and bounds; it was time to sort this out once and for all.

The consultant called it an Abdominoplasty; I called it a tummy tuck. He was on his knees in front of me, with a large fold of skin in his hands. The procedure would remove this layer of skin, re-site my belly button and tighten some surface, fascia muscle. He explained that my abs underneath were a washboard (I had done so many crunches!) and that my hours at the gym would never take away this layer of dead, grey-blue, stretched skin no matter what I did.

My embarrassment at this point was thankfully shielded; Phil sat the other side of a blue curtain, unaware of the silent tears that flowed down my cheeks.

He had come along to support me, while very clearly stating that he had no opinion on what I should do; that I should choose for me. It was a challenge for me to be strong, but I knew this was something I had to do for me – not for vanity, but for my sanity.

Waking up from the surgery, once the woozy feeling had subsided, I began the journey of healing. This started with standing up: not simple when you have been stitched from hip to hip. The operation involved removing a melon shaped slice of skin and flesh, then pulling down the good skin and attaching it to my bikini line. - who knew skin could even stretch that far? My black cat tattoo now resided several inches lower and I had a new belly button!

On my first visit to the bathroom I was doubled over – terrified of ripping those stitches and my fragile skin. Gradually over the afternoon I was able to stand and armed with a million instructions and some very interesting undergarments I was sent home to fend for myself.

Phil had been in America for work and so my lovely friend Katharine had driven me to and from hospital, chatting away at either end to take my mind off of the enormous job in hand.

Within an hour of getting home, Phil arrived having come straight from the airport. Despite being jet lagged and weary, he cooked us all tea and made sure I was comfy.

When I showed him my 'knickers' that went from my ribs to my knees with a thousand hooks and eyes down each side he simply said, "Sexy!" with a mischievous smile. These were to be worn night and day for the next six weeks, to give my new shape every chance of recovery.

Over days and weeks the stitches healed, the scar faded and I started to look in the mirror again. The scar, although long, was really neat and was so low any bikini would cover it. What had been a battlefield of dead and hanging skin was replaced by the smooth, taut skin of my upper abdomen. My tattoo had survived the journey south without a mark and the tiny stitches in my belly button reminded me of the sun's rays.

The baggy tops were gradually replaced by more fitting clothes, although it took me a while to stop the habit! Gradually 12s and 14s replaced the size 18 and even 20 tops I had worn to hide in.

The best feeling in the world was when Phil traced a lazy finger down over my ribcage and across my tummy. It was such a sensual act and he had always loved me for who I was, only now I could love it too. My tummy had carried both of my beautiful children, but it had also carried so much heartache: the rejection when Kassi was born; the gut wrenching loss of my Gramp; the sinking feeling when I realised my marriage was over and the fear in its pit when my life was threatened by my now ex-husband.

The weight of it all had proved too much and I had loathed the area where it all lived. I had tried to fix it myself, through lots of inner and outer work.

I had got to 'quite like' and then love the rest of me over the years, but no matter how I tried, finally that part of me had needed some medical intervention.

A friend asked one day, "So what are you having done next?" In that moment I realised that any other improvements could be done with a mind-set shift and some healthy habits. It wasn't about a perfect, shiny Hollywood image. It was removing that daily reminder of the battles that were now gladly behind me.

NICOLA GREEN

Nicola is an international speaker, providing menopause presentations in the workplace and community. Nicola is a wife, mum of two and her favourite pastimes include walking along the beach, paddle-boarding and devouring regular cream teas!

Nicola was 32 when she first went to the doctors to ask, "Could I be going through the menopause?"

Nicola lived the peaks and troughs of her menopause journey for the next 6 years until the age of 38, when she decided her life needed to change.

With such passion to openly share her own experiences, Nicola continues to help break the taboo subject of the menopause and receives the most amazing feedback.

nicola@nicolagreenconsultancy.co.uk

www.nicolagreenconsultancy.co.uk

https://facebook.com/nicolagreenconsultancy

Girl On Fire

My dad's speech at my wedding included this, "Nicola has always shown determination in everything she does. I am going to take you back some 22 years to the night she was born. Threats of being induced by the doctors were enough for her to decide she was determined to show her independence and come into this world of her own accord!"

My journey

I was 32 when I first walked into the doctor's surgery, accompanied by my 3 year old son to ask if I could be menopausal. Many would wonder why I would even consider asking that question at such a young age, but I knew my body was showing signs of the menopause and I also knew that my mum had gone through an early menopause in her early 40's.

The doctor agreed to a blood test, which came back normal and I then decided I was just an exhausted mum of two young children (back to being permanently exhausted) and I needed to pick myself up and 'get on with it', which I continued to do.

However, by the age of 35 I was struggling to just 'get on with it'. I remember the school Summer holidays of 2015, I was working 2 days a week. On the days I was not at work I was asleep on the sofa every afternoon. I have always regularly exercised, whether that be running, cycling or attending the gym, but I had no energy to do any of it. My periods were extremely heavy and every three weeks and my mood was low.

There were many conversations with my husband over these years. Here is one of them...

"What is it that you want? You have a nice house, two healthy children, we go on lovely holidays and I don't stop you from doing anything you want to do." There was no answer from me apart from, "I don't know." I had no emotion, I felt numb and nothing anyone did could make me feel happy. This question was repeated many more times over the following years.

I knew I didn't feel right and decided to contact my doctor who agreed to do the 'tiredness' blood tests; iron, thyroid etc. but also wanted to send me for ovarian scans. You can imagine how the worry of this added to the already low mood. The ovarian scans were clear and the blood test results showed that I was slightly lacking iron, so I went on iron tablets for a month. I was pleased, as I had been iron deficient during both pregnancies and the tablets had given me the energy I was missing. Unfortunately, this was not the case this time. After a month on the iron tablets I went back to see my doctor and explained that I didn't feel any better. I again suggested that I felt I had menopause symptoms and asked for the specific blood test. My doctor agreed, but explained that it was very unlikely to show anything.

A few days later I received a telephone call from the doctor's surgery to say they had received the result of my blood tests and that it showed, quite clearly, that I was perimenopausal. The doctor on the telephone expressed his shock and asked me how I felt. My reply was that I was not shocked, only relieved. I was relieved to know that how I had been feeling over the past 3 years was not just me but there was a reason why. When my husband arrived home that night, I was delighted to be able to tell him that I was not just a miserable cow!

However, within a week, I must admit that I suddenly felt very old and quite emotional about it. I am not someone who often cries, but I remember telephoning my mum, crying and saying I am not ready to deal with this. I suddenly felt like I was living in the body of someone 20 years older than me.

The doctor wanted me to have another blood test in 3 months' time to ensure both concluded the same result. The second test did not show the same result, so we decided to leave it and see how things went. By this time I was feeling brighter again, but my periods were still extremely heavy and I suffered with flooding.

My symptoms seemed to come in 6 month cycles and with varying symptoms each time, which gave greater reason to never be sure whether it was the menopause I was dealing with or not.

2016 was a really tough year. My mother in law was diagnosed with pancreatic cancer in February and very sadly died in October. To try and keep a focus and do something positive during this horrendous time, my husband and I decided to train for Ride London, which is a 100 mile bike ride through London in July. My training started in March and it was brutal! I suffered from complete exhaustion and terrible joint pain, but believed it was all part of the training process and soldiered on through.

Once again, during 2016, I was trying to understand whether my body and mind were dealing with the pressure of the inevitable outcome of my wonderful mother in law's diagnosis and the effect it was having on the family, the exhaustion of my training or the menopause. Ultimately, I was potentially dealing with a combination of them all and it was a very difficult time. In November 2016 I was back at the doctors asking for my bloods to be checked again. This time my levels only showed slightly and not as dramatically as 2015 and my doctor was not concerned so I carried on.

By the end of 2017 I had two more blood tests, which showed I was perimenopausal and my doctor started talking to me about Hormone

Replacement Therapy (HRT). My doctor was concerned about the risk of future osteoporosis. I was 37 and I didn't feel that I knew enough about HRT to commit to it and I wasn't ready to seriously consider committing myself to 10+ years of medication at this stage. Even though I had been through an extremely tough year, I was feeling better in myself and as much as I was dealing with some symptoms, I felt that with a good diet, strength training and good exercise I could manage my symptoms.

I also had a friend who had been through a premature menopause without HRT and had come out the other side and so had my mum. I felt that if I was going through the menopause, I would rather tackle it head on and get it 'over and done with'.

I was 38 when this thought process changed.

For three straight months during the summer of 2018 I suffered a whole wave of symptoms and all in one go.

I had suffered from a few night sweats in the past, but was never sure if they were really a night sweat or whether I had just wrapped myself up in the duvet too tightly! I soon came to realise they were night sweats and I was suffering from more. I would wake in the middle of the night with water running down the back of my neck and my body wet. I would wake in a sudden shock and then realise what had happened. The duvet would be thrown off and I would then cool down and try and get back to sleep. This was repetitive. However, I came to learn there was a trigger to my night sweats - chocolate!

I was also suffering from the inability to be able to fall asleep at night. Often this was just because my body felt like it was on fire or having hot flushes. I would do the 'duvet on-duvet off' action. I would be trying to get to sleep, naked with cold flannels on my head and on my feet! I suffered terribly with what felt like burning soles of my feet.

Before realising some of the triggers to my lack of sleep, hot flushes and night sweats, I spent three months dealing with sleep deprivation. Most nights I would finally get to sleep at around 3am/4am in the morning to then get up again at 7am to get ready for work and the school run.

Adding to this was the fact I had not had a period for over three months and this was the first time, since the delayed period at the age of 32, that I had missed a period in the six years of my journey. The fact I was still having periods also made it difficult for me to believe I was menopausal, as it was the first question the doctors asked me, "Are you still having periods?" The answer had always been "yes" and therefore they always doubted my reasoning to be menopausal.

The lack of periods, sleep deprivation and sheer exhaustion at this time led me to a place where I was struggling. The work ethic that had been instilled in me as a child was part of me and therefore work got everything I had to give. Now I knew, once again, my home life was suffering.

Crunch point...

A Thursday afternoon at about 4pm and I had just dragged myself through my 3 days of work. I arrived home, collected my son from school and I was completely and utterly exhausted and emotionless.

My husband came home from work and I was at the kitchen sink washing up. He asked me if, on Saturday, I could take our daughter to one town 30 miles away in the morning and another town a further 30 miles away in the afternoon.

I stood at the kitchen sink, looked him in the eye, put my head in my hands and said, in a whisper, "Don't ask me to do anything else." I remember this moment because he looked back at me and said, "I can see you can't do anything else." I felt like I wanted to fall to the floor and cry it all out, but I couldn't; I had no emotion.

Enough was enough. I was bored with myself and the person I had become and decided I was going back to the doctor to either ask for antidepressants (which I had never taken before) or a further blood test and HRT.

I had a blood test which showed conclusively that I was going through a premature menopause and my doctor was now recommending I started HRT due to my risk of osteoporosis. For me, it was nothing to do with osteoporosis; I just needed to try and get some part of my life back.

The transformation...

Within 3 days of taking HRT the black cloud lifted. I could finally see clearly again and it made me realise that I hadn't been seeing clearly for a very long time.

I started to rebuild myself and my life. I really started to look into my self-care; what I was eating and drinking and how it affected me. I learnt some mindfulness and ways to relax, but more importantly it allowed me to be 'me' again.

It did take my body at least 3 months to settle on HRT and, even now, I feel I like I go through peaks and troughs of emotions, but nothing to the extent of what I was experiencing before.

After rebuilding myself as a person, I started to consider whether my career was still the right one for me. I personally felt I had lived in quite a negative way for a long time (those closest to me would have been the only ones to realise this) and I didn't want any negativity in my life anymore. I decided it was time for a change of career. I had been in the same profession since leaving school and I needed to know what else was out there for Nicola Green.

I quit.

I don't know if I have 'quit' anything in my life, but I was no longer the 'vulnerable' woman I had been over the previous years. I was back and so was the determination.

Many friends, family and colleagues thought I was mad but I had to try something new even if I had no idea what that was going to be!

Within the first few weeks of my HR course the CIPD sent out information about the menopause in the workplace and how it was still a taboo subject that needed addressing. This was my light bulb moment. This was me. I had lived and worked through this and I was now passionate about ensuring others didn't struggle the way I did.

I worked on it, I researched it, I put together marketing literature and then it was time to present it!

My first presentation was in Mum and Dad's living room with a couple of mine and my mum's friends.

Bingo!

This was me. This worked and now I had the reassurance to push it forward. I marketed my presentations and I started to get bookings. I was on a roll and for someone who had never presented in front of an audience in her life, I was a natural!

My biggest achievement and probably my best ever presentation came two months later to an audience of 74. The connection I had with the audience, the buzz felt by the attendees and the emotion shown, was truly overwhelming.

I remember driving home from that presentation playing (at full volume) Alicia Keys - Girl on Fire and singing my heart out.

I was right. It was a thing and I had made it happen. I was back.

RUTH BRUCE

Ruth is a Virtual Assistant, kind of like a freelance PA. A data nerd with a background in project administration, Ruth has a passion in numbers that helps small business owners fulfil their own passion. She has a genuine interest in giving them more time to focus on the bigger picture, on their priorities and on the things that need their personality stamp. If you're constantly overwhelmed with the volume of business tasks, contact Ruth at:

info@ruth-bruce.com

www.ruth-bruce.com/

https://linkedin.com/in/ruthbruce/

https://facebook.com/RuthMBruce/

https://instagram.com/brucelooseabootthishoose/

Living Life On The Bounce - My Lifechanging Stoma

"My mission in life is not merely to survive, but to thrive; and to do so with some passion, some compassion, some humour, and some style."– Maya Angelou

I was diagnosed with Ulcerative Colitis (UC), aged 28. I'd been suffering with stomach upsets and diarrhoea for a few weeks and went to the Doctor because I had blood in my stools. Most people with UC are diagnosed after a few months or even years but, luckily for me, my GP spotted the symptoms straight away. He was a newly qualified GP who had studied Colitis and Crohn's, another type of Inflammatory Bowel Disease (IBD). Both frequently confused with Inflammatory Bowel Syndrome, but a whole different kettle of fish.

At the time I'd heard of Crohn's but not UC and I had absolutely no idea about the symptoms or how it affects your life. When I had my first 'flare-up' (in my case, my large intestine became inflamed, ulcerated and the ulcers burst) my GP prescribed me steroids and immunosuppressants. The first of many drugs. They stopped the bleeding fairly quickly, but the side effects were something else. Immunosuppressants made me constantly nauseous, along with steroids which had several side effects (including irritability and constant tiredness). Iron tablets can give you constipation, resulting in piles. After a while on steroids you get 'moon face' where you end up looking like a deranged yellow chipmunk! You can't come off steroids all at once either, you have to gradually reduce the dosage over several weeks; it's not surprising that IBD sufferers call them the 'The Devils Tic Tacs'!

You get used to UC pressing the reset button on your life every ten years or so and having to start again. Death, divorce, redundancy, I've been through all those and there is no guarantee what could trigger a flare.

I was the only person in my family with IBD. I often felt that there was no one to talk to about it. Whenever anyone initiated a conversation, they quickly went green and ran away if I started going into the gory details. Nobody wanted to hear about how the pain was like having ground glass and acid working their way through your intestines. Blood in your poo, sometimes only blood, pooping blood into the toilet. Most times I glossed over the symptoms to avoid feeling awkward because conversations could sound like a horror movie. Nowadays Crohn's & Colitis UK have a closed Facebook group for anyone affected by IBD.

People don't understand. I got used to not telling people that I had UC because instead of seeing you as who you are, they often labelled you as 'that girl with that condition'. I tried not to get frustrated by people making assumptions, like 'stress causes a flare up'. People telling you to pace yourself, as if I hadn't thought of that after having this condition for almost 30 years.

Leaving the house could be an adventure, as you had no warning of the urge to poop. I always scoped out the nearest toilets whenever I went out and the fastest route to them. I had a running joke with my family about using rugby moves and jinking through the opposition to get to the loo first. My family were convinced that I'd rugby tackle people to get to the toilet to avoid pooing my pants! I had a lot of empathy with my nieces and nephews when they were potty training.

Life went back to normal once my initial flare up got under control, apart from having to take a 'maintenance dose' of drugs every day to reduce the chances of flaring. Over the years I grew to know the signs for when I'm heading towards a flare and could talk to my GP and take preventative measures, including more medication if necessary. I became an expert in managing my condition, so much so that even my family and friends were surprised by how much a major flare could affect me.

I divorced my first husband, that's a whole other story, and met Graham. I told Graham that I had UC but he hadn't seen me having a major flare. It can be difficult telling people about your condition when starting a relationship because you have no idea how they will react. I was very lucky and though Graham didn't realise how bad it could get, it wouldn't have mattered to him anyway.

I had a few mini-flares and managed to stay symptom free for about eight years, then I had a doozy.

The disease had been rumbling over for a few months and the steroid tablets weren't being effective, so I went into hospital to have steroids on a drip instead. I was expected to be in for 24 hours but unfortunately my body decided that it didn't like the intravenous steroids. Six weeks later I was still in hospital, after having who knows how many drugs pumped into every orifice. My eldest daughter Kayleigh was about nine years old at the time and got used to visiting me in hospital almost every day. I remember crying in my room after four weeks in hospital with no sign of remission, it makes social distancing sound like a piece of cake.

My large intestine became fully inflamed and I was scheduled for an operation to remove it and to form a stoma. A stoma is where a bit of your intestine is poked outside your body through an opening in your abdomen and your 'output' goes into a bag which is attached to your stomach. Graham rang around the family to tell them about the surgery. He was my 'rock' and hid just how upset he was from me. I found out later how he struggled emotionally when he was making the calls. People don't realise how much chronic illness can affect your partner and your family.

By that time, I'd had enough and was desperate to have the surgery. I was so disappointed when it was cancelled on the morning of the operation because I had 'turned the corner'. The ward team sent the surgeon into my room because I refused to leave the hospital with my large intestine intact. I begged him to do the surgery but he said he wouldn't do it unless it was absolutely necessary.

The following year I fell pregnant with my youngest daughter Catriona. Graham and I got married in 2012. After Catriona was born, I had 15 years with mini- and micro-flares until 2019 when I had a major flare up with very little warning. I went to the GP, was sent straight to hospital and was an in-patient for a week on intravenous steroids and saline. I ended up having one drip in each hand so had to do the 'dance of the drip stands' when going to the loo unless a nurse was available to disconnect me. Catriona remembers that I had to have a low-fibre diet because too much fibre put stress on my colon. This goes against the advice from nutritionists and health experts to eat colourful foods with lots of fibre, but giving me that much fibre would have overloaded my system.

During my stay, my consultant and the surgeons said that surgery was an option. After talking with Graham, we decided to go ahead with the surgery. I had the operation a couple of months later on 1st July 2019 and it's given me my life back.

I did my research in the two months before my surgery. I found the ColostomyUK Facebook Support Group, a private group for ostomates to share their thoughts and experiences of life with a stoma. Bristol Ostomates Self Support Group invited me and my family to their Open Day, which gave us the opportunity to meet stoma bag suppliers, take a look at the different products and chat to other people with stomas, which settled any qualms I had before the operation. It was amazing to speak with people who had experienced stoma surgery and were not only carrying on with their lives but enjoying the benefits of having a stoma.

Southmead Hospital even had an 'induction' for people booked in for stoma surgery and their partners so you knew exactly what to expect before, during and after surgery. The surgery took about five hours and I had a meal a couple of hours afterwards. The next morning one of the stoma nurses came in and showed me how to change my bag. I went home four days later when I was confident changing my stoma bag and managing my stoma. There are follow up appointments with the stoma nurses too.

It took a little while for me to get used to having a bag; there were a few teething troubles, but it has given me a new lease of life. Because UC was part of my life for so long, I didn't realise until after the surgery just how much it affected us all. The impact on me and on my family was slow growing and had a gradual and cumulative effect, always there in the background. It's strange living without pain, or the anticipation of it, after so many years and it takes time to get used to.

Within months I started my own Virtual Assistant business (more details in my bio).

Remember to enjoy the good times, live your life and keep taking the tablets! I've done the Couch to 5K running challenge three times between flares, my husband and I ran the Bristol 10K and ran 10K with Ben Smith, the 401 Challenge Runner. I got really good at living my life 'on-the bounce' - being in a state of readiness and awareness and thinking one step ahead, probably why I'm so organised. There are some inspirational resources for people with chronic conditions, like the IBD Runners & Riders Facebook Group and Mesha, aka Mr Colitis Crohns. In 2020 I started the Couch to 5K again and I celebrated my first stomaversary with a run. There is no stopping me!

You're still the same person you were before you were diagnosed, you're still you. You'll have good times and bad times; enjoy the good times and accept that shit happens, and in our case it really does! Find someone you can trust to talk to, who will take things seriously and not have a wobble when you talk about poop. Try not to worry if people appear thoughtless and inconsiderate, it's just that they don't understand. Try to see the funny side because they aren't going to stop saying things with the best intentions.

Don't be nervous to ask your stoma nurses for advice, that's what they are there for. Talk to your surgeon and surgical team, they want you to ask questions and be confident in your decision to have surgery; they really have heard it all before. Search the internet for local self-support groups and check if there are local 'listeners' you can phone and chat to. Check out stoma suppliers but don't get too hung up about detail before surgery because different bags suit different people and the nurses will guide you.

Thanks to my surgeon Mr Smith, my stoma nurses and the Southmead Hospital team who were all brilliant from pre-op onwards. Nurses, doctors, consultants, surgeons, catering and cleaning team are all lovely and always make time for a chat and the personal touch. I cannot thank them enough for all of their support.

SIOBHAN PANDYA

Siobhan Pandya, born and raised in Scotland, now resides in Dallas, Texas with her husband, Rupesh and two amazing sons, Ronan and Keaton.

While she loves to spend time with her precious family and friends, she also finds time to help others through her volunteer work. She is currently a Council Member at ACCA (Association of Chartered Certified Accountants) supporting their mission to lead the accountancy profession by creating opportunity.

She is also a Board Member at First Candle, working to end SIDS and other sleep related infant deaths. Siobhan is always guided by her angel, Cailen.

siobhanpandya@gmail.com

www.firstcandle.org/

https://linkedin.com/in/siobhan-pandya-fcca-4781857/

Why Me? Why Anyone?

Warning: This chapter contains references to Baby Loss

Life is full of many difficult decisions. As I sat in our apartment, scrolling through pages of nursery designs, I thought I was making one of those decisions. Little did I know that the most difficult decision of our life was yet to come.

Each doctor's appointment was the same.

"You are doing great, the baby is doing great, everything is on track," the doctor would say.

This is exactly what every first-time mum wants and expects to hear. At our 36 week appointment, which included an ultrasound, the message was no different. In fact, we had started counting down to the baby's arrival in days instead of weeks. We went home and followed the same routine and yet something felt strange that night. I sensed a fluttering sensation in my belly and immediately convinced my husband to take me to the hospital. I knew my body and I knew something was wrong. They quickly admitted me and started monitoring us, but not long after came the news that the baby was in distress and there needed to be an emergency c-section.

The next couple of hours were a whirlwind of emotion, adrenaline and exhaustion. Our baby, Cailen, was rushed to the NICU and I was left to rest. A little while later, the doctor slowly walked into my room. She said that what I had been feeling was Cailen having seizures due to the umbilical cord wrapping around his neck and affecting the blood and oxygen flow to his brain. The chances of that happening were close to one in a million – I was that one.

We asked what life would be like for him and she hesitated, then she said, "He's not going to make it. I am sorry. We have him on a ventilator for now." As she left the room, I looked at my husband Rupesh, shook my head and asked him to double check; they must have the wrong baby, they must have a medicine, they must be wrong, they have to be wrong. They were NOT wrong. As Rupesh and I sat in disbelief, we tried to figure out why this was happening to us. It didn't matter how many times we asked the question; the answer was the same each time – we don't know.

We did know one important thing; he was our baby and we were his parents and NOTHING was going to change that. In that moment, we promised each other that we would be the best parents that we could be to our little man. Everything after that moved rapidly; family and friends were called; tears were shed and plans were made. I had just had a c-section, but was not going to let that get in the way of me holding and loving my baby. There would be time for recovery later. Rupesh and I spent every moment in the NICU telling Cailen how much he was loved, how blessed we were to have him as our son and no matter what, he would always be with us. We even tried to get him to pick his favorite parent!

It was on the third day that we made the most difficult decision of our life: we realized that keeping Cailen on a ventilator was for our benefit, as he was sedated the whole time to avoid further seizures. As Rup and I looked at our baby laying there, we knew we had to do the right thing. We informed the doctors that we wanted to take him off the ventilator. It was now up to Cailen to decide when he would be ready for his angel wings. For the next two days we took pictures, told stories, sang songs and did everything we could to fill him with a lifetime of love. I actually tried teaching him how to spell my name – epic fail!

On day 5, around 9pm, I was holding Cailen when I noticed his vitals changing. I could feel him getting weaker in my arms. As the doctors and nurses rushed to check him, we knew that the time had come to say goodbye. We knew it was going to happen but we were still not ready; just one more hug, one more kiss, one more touch. Then our baby became our angel.

Losing your baby is not something that you ever "get over"; instead you learn to live with the memories. You learn why we are told to think about our wildest dreams but not our wildest fears. You learn that not everyone can provide the support needed. You learn that you have to speak your mind without fear of the consequences. You learn that it is okay to be selfish sometimes. You learn that sometimes there is no answer to WHY.

You learn about YOU.

I have always thought of myself as a strong person; someone that can look at the problem in every situation and find an acceptable solution. During my time in the hospital, I realized that some problems are not meant to be solved; they are just meant to be experienced. My experience with Cailen didn't change who I was, instead it changed who I became as I grew older. When I am in a tough situation, I always look back and compare it to what we went through with Cailen and it makes me appreciate three things:

1. Nothing can be as challenging as that experience (autopsies and cremations are best left for TV shows).

2. I have the inner strength and resilience to deal with anything.

3. I miss my baby so much.

Luckily, we have two more boys, Ronan and Keaton, who provide lots of hugs and kisses to help with number 3! One of the most important lessons that both Rupesh and I learned was that each individual deals with each situation differently. We cried, yelled and stayed silent at different times. But we always made sure that we gave one another the space necessary to process what we were going through. My husband provided support at times when I didn't even know that I needed support and by letting him take my pain for a few moments, or make me laugh, I felt human.

While doing this, we felt that it was necessary to get some help and so turned to a psychologist for support. We appreciated the fresh perspective as we learned about how to listen to one other and how to think about the future at some point. We also explored various ways to relax including reiki (a healing technique using energy), yoga and crystal healing. They all helped in separate ways.

Through the journey, I came to the conclusion that I had to make a choice; the choice between continuing the search for WHY or continuing life with my amazing husband. Deep down, I knew that I would never know why this happened to me, why it happened to us, why it happens to anyone and so I stopped searching for answers (at least in this lifetime!). In my opinion, life starts with an empty toolkit and with each experience, we fill it up with a variety of tools; some forever, some for now.

When I think about our experience and how I can help others, the following 'words of Siobhan wisdom' come to mind:

- Be ready to never know WHY

- Always trust your instinct; it can be the difference between life and death

- When everyone wants you to be quiet, shout the loudest

- Keep an open mind; try new things if you think they will help

- Think about what you are going to add to your toolkit based on your experience

- Accept love and support; it will change your perspective

- Understand that time doesn't heal you; you heal you

- Talk about your experiences with a little humor – it definitely helps others feel more comfortable

- Don't compare your experience to anyone else's – each one is unique

- Be thankful for what you gained; it's more fulfilling than thinking about what you lost

- Don't feel bad about remembering your experience, no matter how much time has passed

- Expect others to move on: this is not their experience

- Similar to airplane life vests, take care of yourself before you try and take care of others

- Chocolate always helps, preferably Cadburys

- It is what it is (this one should be a standard tattoo!)

Both Rupesh and I take comfort from the thought that our angel, Cailen, is watching over us all and that he knows how much he is loved and missed each and every day. We are so fortunate that we can share these experiences together, support one another and watch our boys fill up their life toolkits. Although I will never know why this happened, I know that I will do my best to make sure that it doesn't happen to anyone else, which is why I am a Board Member at First Candle, a not for profit organization working to end Sudden Infant Death Syndrome and other sleep-related infant deaths as well as support families who have had a loss.

But after all these words, the most important point to make is that I would not change any of it. It may sound odd, but I truly believe that everything happens for a reason; I may not know that reason today or any day, but I know that it is a part of our journey, my journey.

This is the life I was given and I need to live it to the best of my ability.

STACEY CAMPBELL

After appearing in Amazon bestseller, The Bounce Back Journey, Stacey was asked to write more of her inspiring journey for this book.

A global pandemic and lockdown did not slow this girl down! Stacey did not stop during lockdown and certainly made the most of her time.

Stacey moved house, flipped a property and wrote her first fictional book. Starting with a few notes in her note pad, less than 12 weeks later Stacey had a 110,000 word, fully edited book that's now with Discover Your Bounce Publishing! The book is due to be released in early 2021. - This girl definitely doesn't let the grass grow under her feet!

https://www.facebook.com/TheStormTrilogyOfficialUK

https://www.instagram.com/the_storm_trilogy/

https://twitter.com/trilogystorm

From A Closing Door To The Dancefloor

I walked as fast as my feet could carry me towards the automatic doors at the end of the familiar corridor. My head was down, my eyes fixated on the floor in front of me. I needed to exit the building as fast as I could. "Don't look up!" I told myself.

I did not want to make eye contact with anyone. I could hear several people calling my name behind me; I ignored them and kept walking, my pace picking up each time I heard my name called. I did not want anyone seeing me in the frantic state I was in.

It was almost impossible to believe this was the last time I would walk out of the building I had spent so many happy years inside of; there were so many wonderful memories. I grabbed hold of the long metal handle on the door, the sound of my wedding ring clanged against it and echoed through me. I gripped onto the handle and pulled it back as hard and as fast as I could.

It was the same door I had nervously entered thirteen years previously. My first day in what I thought would be my forever job. "It wasn't ever supposed to end like this. I thought I was going to work for the company forever," the voice in my head whispered in a panic. I was in shock. I could feel the warmth of my tears as they ran down my face. My breathing was shallow, I felt out of breath. His words barked inside of me once again, "Come back when you're better or not at all."

After complications on the birth of my first child the prognosis from my hospital consultant at the time was that I was not going to make a full recovery. I was left with a permanent disability. How could anyone be so cruel? This was my hour of need, one of the lowest points in my life and mentally I felt shattered. The company I had worked for since I left school was turning its back on me. A feeling of vulnerability washed over me as I breathed in the cool fresh air outside. I was on my own. The world suddenly felt bigger and scarier than it ever had before.

I arrived home and composed myself. My priority: I need to find a job. Another wave of panic washed over me. I have a mortgage to pay at the end of this month and no future income. My parents jumped to my rescue by offering to pay any bills until I had found another job. I thanked them; knowing they were behind me took the financial pressure off my situation, but I was too proud to take any money from them.

I knew I had to find another job as soon as possible. I have never not worked. I have always been very driven, ambitious, and financially independent - I had two part time jobs when I was fifteen years old. Not working was not an option financially as I was not willing to take any handouts that had been kindly offered to me. The next day I received a text message from a family friend asking me if I knew anyone looking for a job. A member of her team had just handed in their notice. It felt like fate, this message could not have come at a better time. The job I was being offered was less hours and less money than I was used to, however it was just about enough to pay all my bills meaning I could survive. I felt relieved; my job hunting was resolved in less than 24 hours. My problems were solved, the big dark cloud disappeared from above me as I accepted the job offer and excitedly waited to start the new role.

I enjoyed working for the company and my confidence started to return. I was happier than I had been in a very long time, earning the least amount of money I ever had. This taught me a valuable lesson - money does not buy you happiness. It did not take long for family and friends to start telling me my eyes were sparkling again, my familiar smile had returned along with my loud bubbly personality. I started to feel like Stacey again.

My father was a DJ in the 1970's & 1980's. Music and flashing disco lights are also two of his favourite things and I have inherited this passion. Three years ago, a friend approached me and asked me if I could do a mini disco for her daughter's birthday party. I initially declined - how could I possibly do a disco? I am not a DJ. I did have a few flashing discos balls and lots of music, but I did not have a disco set. I joked with my father about the request my friend had made. "Do it," he said with confidence. "I'll get you a disco stand and teach you how to mix music; mixing music is the easy bit. The hard bit is having the gift of the gab on the microphone. You cannot be taught that, you either have it or you do not and you've got it." he said reassuring me and convincing me to agree to the disco.

Knowing I had just over 3 weeks to get a set together made me feel uneasy. The first disco terrified me; I hated doing it. I felt nervous, anxious and as it finished, I told myself, "I'm never doing another one." As I was packing down all the equipment several people approached me and asked me if I could do their children's birthday parties. My father had come along for support and answered yes I could do the parties before I had a chance to say no. I glared at him as he agreed to them on my behalf. He looked back at me, shrugged his shoulders and innocently mouthed, "What?"

Another job opportunity presented itself to me. An old work colleague had started up his own mortgage company and he offered the chance to work with him. I said yes and took the job role. I already had banking exams behind me as I was a qualified financial advisor. I needed to complete two other exams to become a mortgage advisor. I studied for the exams whenever I had any free time whist trying to juggle working in the week, DJing on evenings and weekends and raising my three-year-old daughter.

I managed to pass both exams in under six weeks. As my DJing took off, I started taking bookings for local school discos, proms, weddings, 30th, 40th, 50th birthday parties, wedding anniversaries and football presentations. I also had a regular spot at a local pub and I really started to enjoy it. Later that year I got approached by a casino in the city centre, they wanted me as their resident DJ for all of their Christmas parties and their New Year's Eve party.

Fear took over me, I did not believe I was good enough to DJ at a large casino in the centre of my hometown. I politely declined and said I was unable to work for them. The casino did not take no for an answer; I was asked again. I approached my father for guidance who said, "You're good enough, get down there and have some fun!" He smiled at me and winked. I reluctantly said yes to the casino and nervously signed their contract. I felt terrified; completely out of my comfort zone. The familiar anxiety feeling returned the same way it did when I did my first ever disco. I knew the casino had very high expectations and I did not have enough confidence or belief in myself. The voice in my head did not help either as it kept repeating, "What if it's a disaster, you're not good enough."

The discos at the casino could not have gone any better, I enjoyed every bit of all of them. I took a phone call on New Year's Day 2019. "Stacey!" shrieked the general manager of the casino down the phone, "That was the best new year's eve disco we have ever had. Can we book you up for Christmas and New Year in December 2019?" I confidently replied with, "Yes, I'll be there." When the call ended I was left completely speechless, buzzing and on a high. I had smashed it.

I spend a lot of my working week networking. I love it; I am a people person and I naturally bounce off others. A year ago, I was asked if I could give a ten-minute presentation at the end of the next monthly meeting I regularly attended. I agreed, my only thought was what do I talk about? No one wants to hear about interest rates for ten minutes, that is only interesting if you are a mortgage advisor! I decided to talk about my journey over the past six years.

I started from when I was fighting for my life on an operating table to how I had ended up stood in front of everyone on that day. I made everyone laugh out loud and I also made people cry with the emotional parts of my personal life. After I finished talking, Nicky Marshall approached me and asked me if I could share my story in her up and coming book.

My mind said, "No, you can't write, writing is your weakness, you're not good enough!" I reminded myself I thought the same thing about the discos at the casino. Before I had a chance to think I blurted out, "Yes, I'll do it." I then panicked all evening about how I was going to write the chapter I had agreed to do. I am very proud to say the book I featured in became an Amazon bestseller, it climbed all the way to the top 10 in its category. I was overwhelmed with the feedback I got from people who read my chapter. I always believed I was a woman that could not write. Maybe I could?

When lockdown started, I could not work or DJ until further notice. I had a lot of time on my hands and I have never been someone that can just sit still. I thought back to a conversation I had with a friend a few weeks before who said, "Stace, you should write a book, you have a funny way of telling stories." Fast forward three months, I have co-written a book with a close friend and we have written just over 110,000 words. The book has been edited, sent for proof reading and is now ready for publishing all in under twelve weeks. Whilst we only set out to write one book, we enjoyed writing it so much, we thought why stop at one? The book is now part one of a trilogy!

As I was excitedly counting down the seconds to midnight at the casino on New Year's Eve waiting for the new decade to start, I never would have believed within the next couple of months I would feature in a book that has become an Amazon bestseller, or that I would have co-written part one of my very own trilogy. I have learned to stop saying no to anything that scares me. I have started to embrace fear and the opportunities that present themselves to me.

Nothing great or extraordinary can ever be achieved from the safety of your comfort zone. My safe 'forever job' unexpectedly ending as quickly as it did was one of the best things that ever happened to me; it was a blessing in disguise.

I have learnt doors can close on you completely unexpectedly and at the time we question why. It affects us mentally and physically, stealing our confidence as it does not make sense and it can seem unjustified. It is because during this period, we are unable to see the future doors ahead of us waiting to open.

Life has taught me it does not matter how hard or fast you fall, your strength is in your return. It is the height you reach when you bounce back that counts.

SUE TETLEY

Sue works as a Thrive Programme Coach, taking clients through the Thrive Programme. This is a training programme teaching the skills and self-insight to overcome mental health issues and start Thriving. Sue was inspired to start her own business after going through the programme herself. It had such a positive impact, she wanted to help others do the same.

Sue loves triathlons and open water swimming. She is a Mental Health Champion and This Girl Can Ambassador. Sue is passionate about inspiring and motivating women to take up exercise for physical and mental well-being.

www.thrivewithsue.co.uk

sue@thrivewithsue.co.uk.

https://facebook.com/Thrive-with-Sue-1041699635854728/

Thriving

Warning: This chapter contains references to Infertility

It was 2.30 pm on a Wednesday afternoon and I was with my husband in a hotel room in London. We were sat next to my phone waiting to hear from the clinic to see if my last IVF treatment had been a success. We had both agreed this would be the last go; after 7 years, 5 lots of IVF and 6 lots of IUI (less invasive fertility treatment) this was it, my last chance to have a biological child of my own. It was a line in the sand and something we had to live with whatever the outcome. This moment and the experiences of the last 7 years would become a defining moment of my life.

Phil and I got married in our mid 20s. We weren't ready to have a family then, but believed one day it would happen when the time was right for us. We soon found this was not to be. Between us we went through many investigations; seeing a huge array of specialists, multiple blood tests, injections and general anaesthetic for procedures. My husband found out he couldn't father children of his own which was a very difficult time for us both. Despite using donor sperm, the treatment failed as my immune system was destroying all the healthy embryos that were created. It's great to have many natural killer cells in many other circumstances, but not when you want to get pregnant.

The whole experience was an emotional roller-coaster with highs, lows, comedy and tragedy. The treatment caused much physical pain at times, but this was nothing compared to the emotional pain when treatment after treatment failed. Each time I would pick myself back up and try and get fit again. I was fairly resilient and was able to bounce back and carry on most of the time. Mother's Day was always difficult each year and I also started distancing myself from friends with young children or those who were pregnant as I just couldn't handle it emotionally. It was hard for people to understand and they didn't want to say the wrong thing either.

There were times when I did feel really low and at one point everything got too much. It was a combination of the treatment drugs, losing my grandmother and buying a house that we couldn't move into because the beams were rotting and the ceiling was being held up by joists. I couldn't even visit the new house. I felt complete powerless, helpless and a fog existed between me and reality. I got sent home from work crying and had a few weeks off from my nursing job. I refused any anti-depressant; I didn't want to go down that route and after 3 or so weeks I started to pick myself back up again.

The turning point

For the initial years of treatment, I really didn't think I had any choice in how this was going to play out. I felt like a pawn and had no control over my destiny. I believed I was totally powerless to change anything. After seeing a fertility counsellor this started to change and helped us realise we did have a say. She encouraged us to ask questions and not just accept everything. The first two treatments had failed so we wanted to see what could be done differently as we only had one more free go on the NHS. I also started to do some research around different clinics and possible reasons the treatment may not be working.

After the free NHS treatments had failed, we decided to go to this clinic in London. We would have two goes in the London clinic and that would be it. For my own peace of mind, I wanted to throw everything at these last few treatments and have no regrets. That way it would be easier to find peace with the decision to stop if it came to that.

We also started talking theoretically about adoption. At the start of the journey, I never believed it would have come to this, but this was the situation we had found ourselves in. We either had to accept and adapt or succumb to mental health issues, potential bankruptcy and the breakdown of our relationship; all very common for those who continue without a plan.

We knew we had to STOP for our own sanity. There was so much about this situation that was out of our control, but stopping was something we had full control over. An incredibly difficult decision, but I couldn't cope physically or psychologically with any more treatment.

"When we are no longer able to change a situation, we are challenged to change ourselves." - Viktor Frankl

I tried all manner of treatments to help calm myself down and increase the chances of the IVF working. However, the one thing that helped me the most during this time was going through the Thrive Programme ®. This is a mental health training programme that teaches people the skills and resources to overcome mental health issues and learn to thrive. It completely changed how I was thinking about things and gave me some great tools to use when going through my last treatment.

Phil was really shocked by how calm I was in the hotel room, waiting for that last result to come back. He was pacing up and down, waiting for the phone to ring. I had rehearsed this moment in my head over and over, imagining being calm and in control and that whatever the outcome, I could deal with it.

The phone rang; I let Phil answer it. I was in the bathroom at the time. I knew from his tone that the news wasn't good. I sat there on the toilet for a while just crying uncontrollably. I came out eventually and Phil gave me a big hug. It was really tough and painful to bear, but there was no choice. I just had to accept that I would never give birth to my own child. I had to go through the grieving process that Phil had done a number of years before when he found out he couldn't be the biological father of a child.

"Retain faith that you will prevail in the end, regardless of the difficulties, and at the same time confront the most brutal facts of your current reality." - Jim Stockdale

Forging a new future

We left it a year after our last treatment, just trying to heal physically and mentally from years and years of uncertainty and treatment. After completing the Thrive Programme, I had a list of goals I wanted to achieve over the coming year: get my fitness back by entering a 40 mile local cycling sportif, run a half marathon, lose the weight I had gained and also start my own business. I had rather a eureka moment towards the end of the programme, suddenly gaining the belief that I could do this and help people as it had helped me. I could start putting my psychology degrees to some use and help others forge a positive future for themselves. Suddenly the ceiling had been lifted on what was possible.

Prior to this I had put myself in a box, believing I was a nurse and running your own business was something others do, not me. I began to start believing I really could do anything I wanted in life if I had the belief and confidence.

I really started to change during this year. My husband honestly believed he'd got a new wife. I started embracing new challenges and opportunities rather than avoiding them. I even joined a speakers' club and set up my own book club, which he was really shocked about!

Adoption

About a year after finishing treatment we started the adoption process. Many struggle with this process and the probing questions from social workers scrutinising your life. However, for us it was easy. We had nothing to hide and it was far less gruelling than IVF treatment. We both came from stable families, both lots of parents were still together. I was a paediatric nurse and a mental health professional. I figured if we couldn't adopt, no one could.

The day I met my daughter

Eventually we were matched with an 11 month old little girl and we met her for the first time at her foster carers house. Imagine getting out of your car and knocking on the door of a person you've never met to meet your child for the first time. As soon as that door opens, you know your life will be changed forever. I had been waiting to be a mummy for so many years and now it was about to happen. It's a surreal and amazing experience. I was trying to keep my emotions under wraps as I had no idea how I would react. We finally saw our little girl and all the years and years of physical and emotional pain suddenly drifted away in that moment of seeing her for the first time.

She believed she could so she did

I continued to set myself fitness challenges. Eventually, after some persuading by a friend, I joined my local triathlon club. I didn't join initially as I wrongly believed I would need to be really good at all three disciplines. It was reassuring to see that there were members of all ages, male and female, all with different abilities.

Once I joined, I never looked back; becoming their Welfare Officer, setting up #RunAndTalk events and enlisting some mental health champions. I have taken part in many different triathlons now. As my confidence and ability has grown, I have slowly increased the event distances. I have grown to love open water swimming, can now swim front crawl and completed a 2 mile swim in the Serpentine. After taking part in a half ironman distance triathlon as a team, I am looking forward to completing it solo next year: swimming 1.2 miles, cycling 56 miles and running a half marathon!

Since taking that decision to stop treatment, my life really has taken on a completely different path. I started to run my own business, do public speaking and recently took part in a podcast to help others going through infertility treatment. I also set up a ladies networking group in my local town. I really love my life now, always trying to be a great role model for my little girl. I was really honoured to receive the Female Grindstone Award from my triathlon club and earlier this year was asked if I would like to be a 'This Girl Can' Ambassador to help to motivate and inspire women of all ages to get more active.

The failure of all the infertility treatment was certainly a defining moment of my life and if I hadn't gone through this difficult period, I would not be the person I am today. I certainly believe in the concept of post traumatic growth and flourishing in life despite the difficulties and trauma that have gone before.

"It's not what happens to you, but how you react to it that matters." - Epictetus

We have our little family and it doesn't matter how we got here, it's what we got in the end that mattered.

TAMMY WHALEN BLAKE

A personal development leader, an entrepreneur, philanthropist and an unwavering optimist devoted to guiding professionals and business owners to live a balanced yet successful life - uncovering their success factors, making a significant impact, focusing their mind, improving productivity and performance.

Tammy courageously left the corporate world and launched a successful coaching business without any substantial resources or systems to run like clockwork, grew an empowered team to achieve the mission and have the freedom to do more in less time. She has seen many go on to start, exponentially grow or diversify their business or careers, so they can design a fulfilled and purposeful life.

www.gotoyellow.co.uk

https://1.gotoyellow.co.uk/get-access

https://facebook.com/Go-To-Yellow-with-Tammy-Inspiring-Change-103498147820118

https://instagram.com/go.to.yellow/

https://linkedin.com/in/tammy-whalen-blake/

My Bounce Back Story After A Redundancy

I was climbing the ladder of life! I was on an upward trajectory and living the dream: dream job, dream car, dream house, dream bank balance – I had it all! I worked in a global tech company and I was climbing the career ladder; the ladder we are all moulded to believe is the ultimate in success. With this came the material possessions as well as the lifestyle of travel, fine food and all the things that not many 25 year olds are fortunate enough to experience. I believed that my worth was determined by my status, which was governed by how successful I could become in my work.

Whilst this served me well for a long time, propelling me further and opening up incredible opportunities, it also magnified the blow when redundancy struck. I had the naïve view that it couldn't happen to me; I had always felt safe and secure.

When I was made redundant the sheer pain of rejection crippled my body, mind and spirit. At first, I had my financial safety net to keep me secure even though, deep down, I felt like a failure. Contemplating this now, I can see that the failure wasn't in me but the company I had invested myself in; I was living those feelings through my own emotions. How could I have lost something that I had built my life around? How could I recover from this? It was like I had experienced a trauma.

My days were mixed with optimism and drive, self-pity and fatigue. I spent hours reflecting on what I could have done differently and getting into bad habits and an unhealthy lifestyle; I can confirm that Smarties DO NOT have the answer! I was feeling all of the emotions whilst navigating my way through the darkness, looking for answers and comfort.

Rejection hurts. It felt like a physical blow and with any physical injury, there is always a period of healing. Just because the injury can't be seen doesn't mean it will hurt any less and as I started to heal, I realised that instead of being bitter, I had to harness the emotions positively to motivate and drive me. There were many tough days, but I needed to stay focused and take the wins along with the setbacks. Dwelling on the past and the pain is easy, but the action we take to move forward is what really matters!

I came to the conclusion that I had already proved myself in a high performing role and so I could replicate it within another company. I had a great CV of experience and so I put my big girl pants on and started applying for roles within companies such as Facebook, IBM, Amazon, Google and more. My applications became interviews and I felt on top of the world again. Every door that opened would quickly close, but I continued to push on.

Looking back I can see that my ego kept me focused on the next big thing, but it was actually blinding me from the truth. I kept telling myself that I couldn't work for a company other than a blue-chip organisation. The thought of going backwards killed me inside and I was afraid. With my ego damaged, I felt alone and hopeless. I had lost my direction and I was adrift with no way home.

During the dark times, it's hard to see, but there's a special kind of force that often shows up in our lives. Some call it luck, some call it God, some call it the Universe. The more you are aware of it, the more it appears, but for a long time I resisted it. I thought it was all fluff and woo-woo and a little on the crazy scale.

I continued to ignore the signs the Universe was sending me. I clearly wasn't ready to receive them; how could I when I had always been surrounded by so much masculine energy? If it wasn't logical, then I didn't have time for it. Thankfully, I gradually lowered my guard and I started to see the signs and accept the lessons that I was being taught.

This force was the turning point for me and when I embraced its existence, I found a shift in my vision of life and what I needed to feel fulfilled. Not Michelin Star fulfilled, not flashy car or status symbol fulfilled, but a deep and peaceful acceptance that I was meant to feel the pain of my experience and use it to shape my own future. To grow into the person I was always meant to be.

In the past decade I have evolved; not only with the natural cycles of life, but I have learnt so much more about who I am and what I want to align to. For too long, I fought against changes that I didn't think I needed. I have realised that I was wasting my energy pushing against something that had to happen, to help shape me into who I am now. It's true, resistance *is* futile!

Changing direction wasn't a sign of weakness or failure, but an indication that my evolution has brought me to a place where I am confident in myself and have a renewed view of how I can achieve success.

By living and striving to achieve someone else's goals and dreams, I had taken away a part of my humanity and a light that I didn't realise had to burn, in order to feel fulfilled. It's funny how we are conditioned to believe this story, whether it feels right or not!

I have learnt that, although it had brought me many privileges, technology didn't actually excite me. It was validation that pushed me to chase what others expected of me and what society suggests we conform to.

My joy comes from empowering myself and others; giving people the tools to find the light in their own lives. I want to help people lean into their best selves and discover *their* joy through living mine. Every morning I wake up excited to learn about human behaviours, how to have healthy habits and become fulfilled. Is it any wonder that the Universe was closing all of the doors that I believed I wanted to open? The signs were there; technology is not my passion – people are!

I believe many of us suppress our true desires and confuse them with external validation similar to my initial ideals. The sad truth is we overwork to prove our worth instead of choosing a life that brings us fulfilment and true happiness.

We are all unique and have an inbuilt purpose to serve, but this purpose can be misaligned if we don't listen to ourselves intently enough. Although I believe that my behaviours and thought patterns are unusual, they truly are my superpowers and only now can I see that they are what make me, me! Now, I embrace them and gift my energy to those I spend time with through Personal Development Coaching.

Whilst redundancy was a difficult time, it also opened up new opportunities to reinvent myself. My advice is that through adversity always comes a lesson. We may not see it at the time, but instead of dwelling on all of the bad situations we have found ourselves in, we should look at the lessons and knowledge that we have acquired through those times. Always ask, "What have I learned?"

The journey to the new you begins with the destination in mind! No one knows what the next 10 years holds, so learn to leverage the skills and passions you have today without those negative thoughts that hold you back. Dream big with your vision.

Set yourself a goal for the next 5 years and make a plan to mark the milestones as you reach them. You could set your intention to apply for a different job, to learn a new skill or to start your own business. Then look at what you need to do to achieve these goals. Try to achieve something every day that will bring you a step closer to your long-term vision, no matter how small!

Keep pushing, be innovative, or do something outside of your comfort zone. As long as you keep learning, it will eventually lead you to success. There is no right or wrong in this, it is a process; a journey to self-discovery.

The way my life looks today may not have been a part of the original plan, but I am certain that the Universe has wonderful things in store; it's a comforting feeling!

Running a successful coaching business has gifted me a life of freedom, excellent health, the opportunity to find my passion and humbling fulfilment. Isn't that a better life than chasing the societal milestones and expectations placed upon us?

I choose to be open to the world, listen to the signs and trust my intuition.

TERESA RIDLEY

Teresa is passionate about being an advocate for both Breast Cancer and Domestic Abuse, having personally experienced both.

Following on from her contribution to this book, Teresa is writing a further two books on her journey through both of those difficult periods of her life and how those experiences have moulded her into the person she has become today.

Teresa is now looking forward to developing this new avenue of her career, which started by co-founding Weston Cancer Support Group in October 2019 and hopes to contribute towards other similar projects in the future.

westoncancersg@outlook.com

https://facebook.com/WestonCancerSupportGroup

From Mouse To Lioness

If you were to meet me you would make a lot of assumptions. I have a strong, bubbly personality with warmth and a kind smile. I can mingle easily and make people laugh. The world sees a confident, well dressed woman who is professional, focused and knows what she wants in life.

But personas are just that; something we use to portray who we want people to believe we are. A way of hiding the person or the vulnerability that we don't want others to see, which I liken to putting our make up on in the mornings. I hate going without make up, it makes me feel self-conscious, vulnerable and is a reminder of the small mouse I once was. Going without make up was a place I used to go to, to become invisible and hide from the world outside.

So now, putting my 'face' on every morning, psychologically, has a much more positive effect. It helps me feel more confident and ready to face the day and its challenges head on. It's a small thing but can make a big difference. A bit like making your bed; I make my bed every single morning not only because I like my bed to look nice, but also it's the first achievement of the day. If the rest of your day goes to rat shit, then at the end of that shitty day at least you can climb into a nicely made bed knowing you did accomplish something positive. And let's face it - there is nothing nicer than a made bed to climb into.

It's taken many difficult years to finally come to terms with who I am; to feel comfortable in my own skin and deal with the demons and monsters that have entered my life at different stages.

There will be many of you out there who will have gone through similar journeys of your own, that will be touched by my story as it resonates with you. I hope it helps inspire others to reignite positivity, bring peace and happiness back when you have experienced adversity. To prove there is light at the end of tunnel. In time you will regrow your confidence and self-worth, learn to love yourself and be happy again. We all need hope and that alone can be enough to carry on, even if it's just one day at a time.

You can't change what was, but you can accept your past as part of your life and the journey it's taken you on to become the person you are today.

Acceptance is a good place to start. Accepting the here, now, and what was. Acceptance is not easy, especially when someone has wronged or hurt you, or you're coming to terms with a loss of any kind. If you can acknowledge these wrongs against you, the pain you feel and where you are right now, that's a good starting point on the road to acceptance, healing and change.

Learn to let go, shake off the past; this will lighten your load. To continue your life carrying these burdens with you will feel like a heavy weight and slow you down. It will hold you back and continue to make your heart and mind heavy. I always joked about my virtual 'ruck sack' I carried around with me, full of my past pain, fear, and anger. I would use it as an excuse for my outbursts, but it wasn't good for my mental health and was holding me back from becoming the lion I needed to be. I needed to find a way to get rid of it.

My life has not been an easy one; I was sexually abused from the age of seven, which continued over several years. I was bullied at school, then spent 15 years in a toxic, violent marriage with a narcissistic, bi-polar alcoholic. They destroyed my confidence, self-worth and happiness and killed any ounce of love I had left, leaving me mentally and emotionally drained with PTSD. The mouse I had become had to dig deep to find the courage and strength to walk away.

It took me two years and for him to come home with a bottle of whisky in one hand and shotgun in the other... I knew the day had finally come that if I didn't leave now I was probably going to come out of my home in a wooden box. That's when the reality hit me: it's now or never! If you want to carry on living and see your son grow up, then you have to pack a bag, walk away from your home and business and GO. That's what I did; I walked away from everything with a holdall bag.

The toxic ex being the controlling narcissist he is, went on to destroy the £750k home and business we had put our blood, sweat and tears into over 10 years. He stopped paying the bills, filtered off the cash from the business and sold everything he could physically rip out of the house, including the Aga and log burner. He then trashed what was left, until it was repossessed and worth a fraction of what it had been valued at. After racking up a shed load of debt that he put my name on, he went bankrupt forcing all the debt to come to me, leaving me no choice other than to do the same.

I was coming to terms with rebuilding my life. Luckily, I had a brilliant support network of girl friends who rallied round, buying me slippers and a dressing gown. Those small gestures meant the world. I sofa surfed for a while, working behind a friend's bar just to be able to buy food and survive, until I was able to sell my wedding, engagement, and eternity rings. This gave me the money to rent a flat, buy an old run around car for £500, get some second-hand furniture and buy some clothes to start what was a very frightening, unknown new beginning.

It was the first of many baby steps to taking back control of my life and rebuilding me. There was finally hope. When you hit rock bottom, there are two options; we can succumb to the blackness of despair and roll over, or we can pick ourselves up and slowly brush it off one day at a time. That's the tougher option of course as it takes courage and inner strength, something you don't know you have when you are in those moments of blackness. By having belief in yourself, digging that little bit deeper and getting up every morning, you start on the road to what can only be better than what was.

Then out of the blue - Boom! - there was another bomb shell. I was diagnosed with breast cancer in March 2017. I would lose my right breast, but was given a glimmer of hope as I could have a reconstruction on the same day and my mastectomy was booked for 6 weeks later. It was such a whirlwind few weeks, but I knew all being well that I would still be able to celebrate my 50th birthday in June. My reconstruction was done via the Diep procedure where the surgeon uses your stomach fatty tissue to rebuild the breast as this gives the most natural result.

As with any surgery there are always chances of complications which are highlighted before surgery, but I don't think anyone actually expects to get any… of course, I did! Not in my breast, but my stomach. I had necrosis, which is an infection where the fat dies. It came up like an abscess in my stomach and burst leaving a gaping hole, requiring intravenous antibiotics for 10 days. I came home with a stoma bag to carry on draining the infection until the hole closed from the inside out. Recovery was slow and this complication meant I would require further surgery over the next two years. But I was alive, the cancer was gone and I was blessed that it had been caught early enough.

I arranged a party for my 50th to celebrate still being here, inviting those who had helped me rebuild my life. These people were family to me and I wanted them to know how much I valued them.

Preparations were made and I had something positive to look forward to, maybe this was a turning point? Turning 50 was going to be the start of a new chapter, leaving all the crap behind. After all, they say life begins at 50!

Five days before my birthday, I got a call to say one of my dearest friends had been killed in a tractor accident, I was devastated. This was followed 6 months later by the loss of another close friend. Both of my best girlfriends had become widows within 6 months of each other. The positive year turned into another rubbish one filled with sadness, broken hearts and lives that would be changed forever.

There comes a time in your life where you take a step back and ask, "Why me? How much more crap can one person deal with? Life sucks and it's unfair. What did I do to deserve more heartache and crap to have to dig my way through?" I felt like a broken china doll who needed to be glued back together both emotionally and physically.

During this time I reassessed my life, questioning my relationship and job. I needed to find something positive that I could throw myself into.

I was at a ladies networking group when I met Louise. Lou had also been through breast cancer and we connected with this common ground. While I had been treated at Southmead Hospital, Lou had been treated under Weston General. We discussed procedures and the support offered and given. During the conversation we ascertained that whilst Weston General had a wonderful Oncology team and Macmillan nurses, they didn't have the space for patients to meet. This got us both thinking and after some research we realised there was a real need to set up a breast cancer support group locally in Weston Super Mare.

The group started in September of 2019, initially with only a couple of attendees, but now we have 17 ladies that join us once a month. They talk about any worries they have, discuss symptoms and side effects, have a cry and get a hug. They receive the support of others who have been on a similar journey, understanding the emotional rollercoaster they are on.

We offer a show and tell for those going through a mastectomy and bring in guest speakers who offer holistic well-being options, dietary advice and skin care. We are planning some fun, positive sessions once we come through lockdown. In the short time the group has been going the ladies have bonded and never cease to amaze me with their positivity, laughter and resilience. I am so very proud of every single one of them.

Women are amazing; no matter what life throws at them, they battle on regardless with dignity, courage, determination, inner resolve and strength.

Whilst I am still not where I want to be financially, for the first time in many years I have found inner peace with myself. I am content knowing that my future will be guided by me and my decisions. I am finally getting back the person I once was and I'm never letting her go again! She is becoming the lioness she needs to be; a hunter, with strong instincts on survival.

The reason for me wanting to share my story is twofold. Firstly it's extremely cathartic. Secondly if I can stop just one other person from losing themselves forever by reaching out, offering an outstretched hand with the glimmer of hope that things can and will get better in time, then my journey will have been worth something.

TONIA GALATI

Tonia is a passionate expert in the field of employability and talent development. Her expertise is in creating and delivering top-notch employability and engagement strategies for both students and graduates.

Tonia is the founder of TG Consulting, working with universities and employers, with a strong commitment towards breaking down barriers for students and graduates in employment, particularly surrounding issues of social mobility. She holds a genuine passion for working on new projects and initiatives and, above all, working with students - particularly those who have life challenges, engaging with them to help them realise their true potential.

www.tgconsultingltd.co.uk/

https:// linkedin.com/in/tonia-galati-4438b910/

You Are More Powerful Than Your Fears

Looking back, I think I have always struggled with self-confidence and imposter syndrome, so it was only logical that my feelings of not belonging or being good enough would accumulate and manifest into something much later in my adult life. As a female the pressure to conform to what society expects of us and the increased pressure from social media, portraying the lives and aesthetics of others through a perfect filter, has impacted me immensely over the years. I know lots of great females in my personal and professional networks who feel the same.

Growing up in a small, prominently white, town in Lincolnshire, my sisters and I were known as 'the brown girls'. We faced frequent bullying from our peers and let's face it, teenage girls can be very cruel. Attending an all-girls high school from the age of 12 definitely made me scrutinise myself at length – my academic abilities, feeling pressurised to 'fit in' and constantly being upset about my looks and how I didn't look like everyone else. This led me to spend the remainder of my high school years trying to blend into the background and avoid any opportunity to draw attention to myself.

However, after high school ended things started to look up for me. I went to university, where I envisioned myself completing my degree and later moving overseas. I really enjoyed my time there, despite the feeling of not fitting in still being very present in my mind. I made some lifelong friends and (thankfully) managed to graduate! Still, to this day it remains a complete mystery to me as to how I did, as I never really engaged with my degree as much as I should have.

When I got my degree results through the post I cried for a good hour; mainly in disbelief, but also because the realisation had hit me that I would now have to actually make some decisions about my future. I never had a plan in place for what I wanted to do career-wise and to be honest, I had always just gone with the flow and fallen into things. Eventually, 21-year-old me decided that I would pack up and move to London and make my millions. I did move to London, although I'm still waiting on the millions! Still not knowing what I wanted to do, I took the first job that was offered to me – an interior designer - where I could utilise my degree, because back then it was expected of you.

I did that for a couple of years but was bored out of my mind, so I moved into an office environment and went to work for a professional body. Whilst I enjoyed the environment and my colleagues were great, I found the same old routine soul-destroying and ultimately felt unfulfilled with my work. I wanted to do something meaningful.

Then one day, by chance, I saw an opportunity advertised at a local university, working with students from difficult backgrounds to help them enter employment. It was at that moment that I realised that *that* was what I wanted to do. I wanted to work with students who had no sense of career direction, who felt like they weren't good enough and like they didn't belong. Without a doubt, I sweated through that interview as the feeling of imposter syndrome took over, but I got the job and have never looked back!

However, over the years, I have always put pressure on myself to deliver high standards, so naturally, I often focused on what others might think of me and avoided situations where I could embarrass myself. This has often dictated my decisions and to an extent the direction I have taken in my career.

When I was offered my first job in Higher Education I tried to negotiate taking out any elements of public speaking and presenting out of the job description. Of course, I was unsuccessful and after a long conversation with my sister, realised that putting myself out there publicly was something I would *have to do* if I had any chance of progressing in my career.

Really this was a blessing in disguise, as my anxieties eventually led me into a career that I love, enabling me to help others and, in particular, work with students and graduates who face challenges and barriers in their lives and employment. Much of my work has been focused on helping others build their own confidence and be the best they can be – ironic really.

Ultimately, my determination to make a difference in the lives of others is what did and still does drive me. I was so passionate and I got things done, soon making a name for myself in the industry. I challenged the thinking of others and helped make a difference to so many in a relatively short space of time.

The conversations I have had with students over the years about what they can achieve and the feeling I get when they are offered the job, or when they realise that they alone are their own limitation, is indescribable. It warms my heart and I feel as though I am doing a hobby I love every single day.

Yet the pressure of wanting to do everything perfectly and the guilt of not wanting to let anyone down, including my team, family, friends and students, resulted in me taking on more than I could manage; working 14 hour days and struggling to sleep. I could feel myself losing control and spent a lot of unhealthy amounts of time in the gym, as that was the only thing I felt I could control.

I often used to find myself upset and exhausted from putting on a front and pretending that everything was okay. This, coupled with the constant ruminating at bedtime, resulted in me having regular 'bags for life' under my eyes. I felt completely lost and as though I had no control over anything. This culminated with a serious bout of anxiety, stress and clinical depression in the autumn of 2014. All of the emotions that I was internalising had started to eat away at me and came flooding out. All the plates I was trying to juggle suddenly came crashing down all around me – and they didn't just break, they smashed into lots of pieces.

My world falling around me really made me reflect on life and the things that were making me so sick. I decided I just wanted peace. I didn't want to feel confined to doing things in a certain way, or not being able to work in an environment that was flexible to how and when I wanted to work, when I felt that I could.

Sometimes you wake up and you just don't feel like facing the world. Being employed, whilst many bosses are understanding of mental health, it is very difficult to say, 'I don't feel like it today, I'm not coming in.' So, after a considerable amount of time working within Higher Education, I decided to take voluntary redundancy and set up my own consultancy business. I ripped the support blanket out from underneath myself and I went it alone. But honestly, it is the best decision I have ever made. Never have I felt so relaxed, fulfilled and in control of my work-life balance, doing what I love.

I was never particularly academic, in fact I found learning at school and university quite difficult. All of my achievements post-study have been due to my passion, commitment and hard work. This is often something that I fail to recognise myself, particularly when I receive a request to speak at an event or I am described as a specialist in my field – because why would anyone be interested in what I have to say, right?

The feeling of being labelled a 'fraud' will probably never leave me, but I have learnt to use my network and if I am not okay, I say it rather than letting things build up. I now have coping mechanisms in place and I know my triggers, which I either try to avoid or manage. I would be lying if I said that I don't get knocked down or have difficult days still, but it is all about getting back up. Yes, it is really flipping hard; walking in a downpour is never easy, but the rain and the storm pass and then the sun comes out and things get better.

I have learnt to trust my support network – my sisters, parents and my friends (I have such amazing friends) who have been instrumental in lifting me up and who are there to support me and cheer me on from the sidelines – my very own cheerleading team. I have learnt to push myself out of my comfort zone, to go with the flow, to not worry if I don't have a plan or if I can't control something and above all - I take risks. Whenever I doubt myself, I focus on how far I have come, everything I have faced, the battles I have won and the fears I have overcome.

My advice? Allow yourself to be vulnerable. Spend time with people who lift you up and avoid those who bring you down. Above all, stop wondering if you are good enough and ignore that voice in your head. Do not listen to anyone who says you can't – particularly if that person is you. Believing in yourself is what gives you the confidence to be authentic and vulnerable; from your vulnerabilities come your strengths.

Yes, my story is filled with some broken pieces, but it also features a major comeback and so can yours.

AFTERWORD
by Sharon Critchlow

Life in the 21st Century has presented Western women with more opportunities than ever before. Whether it is exciting careers, travel or control over the size of our families, the options and opportunities are boundless. However, in this era of adulation of the perfect body and the perfect life, many of us can be left feeling inadequate, ineffective and unsupported when life knocks us down. Our lives can isolate us from each other and from the accumulated wisdom and understanding of the health and emotional challenges which have always been part of the journey of women. This book bridges that gap. Sharing stories serves as a powerful reminder of our resilience and each of these stories comes from the author's heart to ours.

In this book we travel the path of women, through their eyes and their experiences. From the loss of a child and post-partum exhaustion to enduring an early menopause and realising there will be no more children. These chapters have reflected on our relationships with men and explored the impact of losing our homes, divorce and abuse. But they have also reflected the love for a father as he struggles with his health and the courage of the policeman who risked his life for one of us. Our brave sisterhood has shared the positive impact of breast cancer, coping with anxiety and deciding when plastic surgery is the way forward. Reflecting upon these journeys I have noticed how often it was the help from one person that made a positive difference. We can all be that person for someone else.

One final thought is from a quote I once saw on a t-shirt, "I am proud of the woman I am today, because I went through one hell of a time becoming her." This is the story of these women; it is the story of all of us.

If you have been affected by a particular chapter in this book, we ask that you talk to someone: a friend, your GP or a specialist. In the reference section of this book we have included helpful organisations which are there to support you. We also have the Discover Your Bounce Community on Facebook and an array of programmes and mentoring to keep you bouncy!

ABOUT DISCOVER YOUR BOUNCE!

Discover Your Bounce has emerged as a group of companies to provide a platform for wellbeing and inspiration, to support each other and to learn from our collective experience.

Discover Your Bounce Publishing specialises in inspirational stories and business books. We provide mentoring for authors and support from inception of your idea through writing, publishing and cheerleading your book launch. If you have an idea for a book, or a part written manuscript that you want to get over the line, contact Nicky or Sharon on the links below.

Discover Your Bounce For Business provides support for employers who want to improve the staff wellbeing, engagement, culture and performance of their business. We work with CEOs, HR Managers or department heads using practical, easy to implement techniques that create instant change. As we go to print, we have worked with over 2000 employees across the country from a variety of industries and have delivered keynotes at some fantastic international conferences and events.

My Wellbeing supports individuals through individual mentoring and online courses to improve their energy and vision. If your get up and go has got up and gone, get in touch and get bouncing or choose your programme at www.discoveryourbounceacademy.com.

Sharon and Nicky are available to discuss speaking opportunities, wellbeing workshops or private mentoring:

> Nicky@discoveryourbounce.com
> Sharon@discoveryourbounce.com

You can also find out more on our website: www.discoveryourbounce.com

JOIN US!

You are now part of our community and we would love you to join our Facebook group –
www.facebook.com/groups/DiscoverYourBounceCommunity.

THE BOUNCE BACK TRILOGY

The original Bounce Back Journey was published in February 2020, with no idea of the challenges that were to come. The series continues with The Bounce Back Journey of Women's Health and The Bounce Back Journey of Men's Health, published in November 2020.

COMING IN 2021

The Bounce Back Journey of Careers and The Bounce Back Journey of Parenting are coming soon – register your interest by emailing us at info@discoveryourbounce.com.

SOCIAL PASSION PROJECT

Royalties from these books fund our Social Passion Project, providing mental health awareness training and supporting other important mental health projects. Read more at:

www.discoveryourbounce.com/socialpassionproject.

REFERENCES FOR UK AND US ORGANISATIONS

Post Natal Depression

https://apni.org/
https://www.postpartum.net/

Anxiety

https://www.anxietyuk.org.uk
https://adaa.org/

Child and Youth Mental Health

https://www.otrbristol.org.uk
https://www.childline.org.uk/
http://teenmentalhealth.org/

Suicide Prevention

https://www.spbristol.org
http://www.samaritans.org.uk or Call 116 123
https://www.papyrus-uk.org (People under 35)
https://www.samaritansusa.org/
https://suicidepreventionlifeline.org/

IBS

https://www.theibsnetwork.org/
https://www.ibspatient.org/

Endometriosis

https://www.endometriosis-uk.org/
http://www.endofound.org

Depression

http://www.mind.org.uk
https://www.dbsalliance.org/

Breast Cancer

https://breastcancernow.org/
https://www.nationalbreastcancer.org/

Cervical Cancer

https://www.jostrust.org.uk/get-support
https://www.nccc-online.org/

Menopause

https://menopausesupport.co.uk/
https://www.menopause.org/

Inflammatory Bowel Disease

https://www.crohnsandcolitis.org.uk

https://www.crohnscolitisfoundation.org

Stoma Awareness

https://www.colostomyuk.org/ (See also #StomaAware)
https://www.ostomy.org/

IVF

https://fertilitynetworkuk.org/
https://resolve.org/

Child Loss

www.cruse.org.uk
https://firstcandle.org/

Sexual Abuse

https://www.thesurvivorstrust.org/
https://www.rainn.org/

Domestic Abuse

https://www.nationaldahelpline.org.uk
https://www.thehotline.org/

Rape Helpline

www.rapecrisis.org.uk
https://thercc.org/get-support/

"Friendships between women, as any woman will tell you,
are built of a thousand small kindnesses...swapped back and forth
and over again."

Michelle Obama

Printed in Poland
by Amazon Fulfillment
Poland Sp. z o.o., Wrocław

63182628R00087